MUSHROOMS OF THE WORLD

Dr. LUCIUS VON FRIEDEN

MUSHROOMS
OF THE WORLD

with 186 color plates by Laura Maggiora

Translated by
RONALD STROM

American Edition edited by
CAROL STURM SMITH

CONTENTS

INTRODUCTION

WARNING

INTRODUCTION

How mushrooms live

The mushroom, the prize of mushroom hunters, is the fruit of a plant: a plant hidden in the ground, in the case of terrestrial fungi; a plant hidden in a tree trunk or a pile of woody material, in the case of lignicolous fungi. Lignicolous fungi are almost always very harmful to the plants they invade. Like any other fruit, the mushroom develops seeds for the reproduction of the plant. These seeds are known as **spores**, and they are microscopic in size; it would take millions to equal the size of a pinch of snuff. The illustration below shows a small cloud of spores falling from the cap of a mushroom, or, more precisely, from the gills or tubes of the mushroom, which are arranged radially under the mushroom cap. When even one of these spores has reached the earth and found a suitable habitat, a filament or **hypha** develops. The first hypha splits and the two new hyphae continue to branch out and finally form the fungus plant, the **mycelium**, or spawn, which then can produce new fruiting bodies.

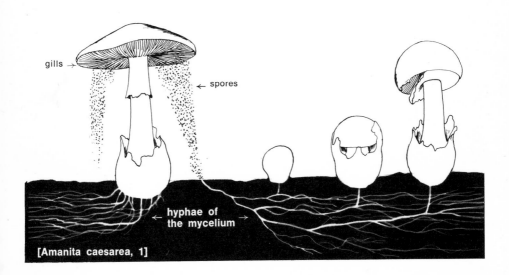

gills →
← spores
← hyphae of the mycelium →

[Amanita caesarea, 1]

11

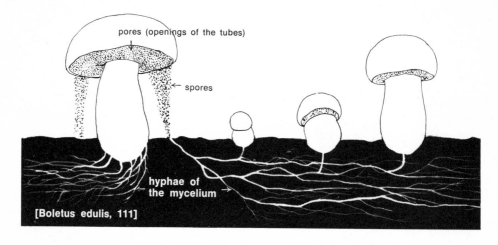

pores (openings of the tubes)

spores

hyphae of
the mycelium →

[Boletus edulis, 111]

The **habitat**, i.e., the suitable environment for the fungus, almost always must be moist and relatively warm. Consequently fungi are rare in winter because of the cold, and in dry summer weather because of the absence of moisture. Nevertheless, there are some species of fungi that survive in cold weather and some that thrive in dry weather.

Some fungi survive only if they manage to join their hyphae to the rootlets of certain trees from which they draw needed sustenance. But it seems that the fungi also contribute to the vegetation of their host trees. If they do not contribute to the host tree, at least they do no serious damage. This relationship of hypha and rootlet is known as **mycorrhiza**, meaning fungus-rootlet. The fungus and the plant joined in mycorrhiza are called, in this and in other similar botanical situations, **symbiotic**, i.e., living together. The Boletes are symbiotic with other plants. Thus the **Boletus (Suillus) elegans** 129 [1] is symbiotic with larches, and it would be useless to try to find this species except in the vininity of larch (see illustration opposite).

Some mushrooms are cultivated commercially. Suitable soil is prepared for them in a damp and warm environment, out of drafts and usually in the dark, and then fragments of fungus mycelium are put in the soil. In a few months the plant develops enough to begin producing fruiting bodies. Only a few mushrooms are grown commercially. In the United States the only mushroom grown commercially is **Agaricus bisporus**, a close relative of the **Agaricus campestris** 24. In Japan the **Cortinellus shiitake** is grown commercially outdoors on evergreen oak, oak, and chestnut wood.

[1] A number following the name of a mushroom indicates its location in the following guide; the same number also refers to the color illustration on the page facing the page of text devoted to the single mushroom.

groups of mushrooms
of the species Boletus (Suillus) elegans 129
and a larch tree, in mycorrhiza

How to distinguish an edible mushroom

Sometimes it is said that an edible mushroom becomes poisonous when grown in one place rather than another. But this is not true. A mushroom remains edible wherever it is grown. One environment rather than another may sustain a certain mushroom, but it cannot make an edible mushroom poisonous or a poisonous mushroom edible.

Sometimes it is said that mushrooms which change color on exposure

13

to the air are poisonous. Actually **Amanita phalloides** 7 does not change color, whether it is touched, cut, or broken; yet is deadly poisonous whether raw, cooked, or dried. On the contrary, **Boletus (Gyroporus) cyanescens** 117 is excellent despite the fact that its inner substance, normally called "flesh", turns bright blue at the first direct contact with the air.

From time to time one hears of various infallible and universal tests employed by some cook or other to determine whether the fungi in his pan are edible or poisonous: the gold ring test, the silver spoon test, the garlic clove test, tests with parsley and milk, and so on. All these tests are fallacious and dangerous. The more universally accepted they are, the more dangerous they become. Many die precisely because people continue blindly to rely on one or another test of this sort.

Even testing suspect species on a dog or cat is of slight use, if at all. Cats and dogs have different digestive systems than man, and a poison that does not affect them may have a harmful effect on man. Doesn't a cat eat rat skin? And don't dogs eat many things that are totally inedible for man? The only foolproof test would be on another human, a test actually applied in past periods of history. If a slave did not die after eating certain mushrooms, then his master could eat them as well. Since this test cannot be applied today, one is obliged to open his eyes: to learn to study and compare the mushrooms he finds with the descriptions and illustrations in the best mushroom guides he finds and to take doubtful but interesting mushrooms to a specialist.

Sometimes, though not always, taste may resolve doubts. Although not all sharp-tasting **Russulae** are poisonous, one should, for safety's sake, discard all sharp-tasting specimens. One should do the same for sharp-tasting or bitter **Lactarii** as well as for the **Boletes**. But this test is useless for **Amanitae**. **Amanita phalloides** 7, which is deadly poisonous, has a pleasant and mild taste. Likewise **Entoloma lividum** 42, poisonous, albeit not deadly, cannot be distinguished by unpleasant taste. Thus the taste test is supplementary and can only be employed when one has already established by other means whether the mushroom in question is an **Amanita**, an **Entoloma**, a **Russula**, a **Lactarius**, and so on.

Gathering mushrooms

Even the most exquisite mushrooms may cause ill effects if they are too mature or spoiled. Do not fill your basket with mushrooms that are too mature or spoiled, or worm- or snail-eaten. Why carry so much home only to throw it away? Likewise, do not gather mushrooms if you are not absolutely sure that they are edible, except for purposes of study. Do not put a mushroom in your basket until you have cleaned it thoroughly. Otherwise it will soil all the others, especially those that have gills. I speak

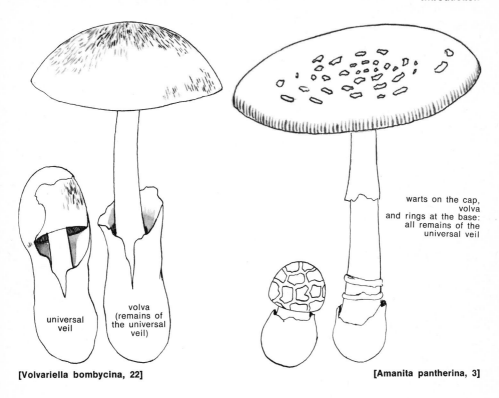

warts on the cap,
volva
and rings at the base:
all remains of the
universal veil

universal
veil

volva
(remains of
the universal
veil)

[Volvariella bombycina, 22]

[Amanita pantherina, 3]

of a basket, because mushrooms are hard-put to remain attractive looking
in any receptacle that does not have firm sides.

But you should not clean mushrooms that you intend to examine for
study purposes. In that case you should keep everything that is on the
mushroom, be it earth, leaves, conifer needles, moss, or snails. Make a
note of the place and weather in which such mushrooms are gathered.
They should be carried carefully so that they are not damaged or disfigured.
One good method it so place each specimen gently in a plastic bag and
then set these bags next to each other at the bottom of the basket or
other container.

In the case of gilled mushrooms, pay particular attention not to leave
the volva unobserved in the earth around the base of the stalk. This
carelessness might have fatal results for an inexperienced mushroom
hunter, leading him, for example, to mistake the deadly **Amanita phalloides**
7 for an innocent and tasty **Agaricus campestris** 24.

Keeping mushrooms

Do not keep fresh mushrooms in a pantry for long periods of time, waiting for a convenient moment to serve them at the table or to dry them for later use. They spoil rapidly and therefore should be prepared or eaten within one or two days of gathering. And the **Coprinus comatus** 28 should be eaten within twenty-four hours, because it spoils extremely quickly. Meanwhile mushrooms should be kept in a cool, well-ventilated place, or in a refrigerator, though not in the freezing compartment.

a) Dried Mushrooms

Some mushrooms can be dried. They should be laid out on shelves in dry airy places in the dark. Sometimes, however, they do not lose their aroma even when dried quickly in direct sunlight. They should not be left outside during the night but put in a dry place. Sometimes, if one wants to dry them quickly and prevent then from spoiling instead of drying, one should boil them first. They can be put in a large strainer, sliced or whole depending on their size, and set in a pot of boiling water. They should be left in the water for two or three minutes. Then they should be carefully drained and laid out for drying. The hot water sterilizes them, killing all the insect larvae and eggs that might otherwise destroy the mushroom. To sterilize them completely, one must make sure that the boiling water reaches the mushrooms in the middle of the mass in the strainer. When they are thoroughly dried they should be kept out of drafts, in plastic bags or covered glass jars. Before dried mushrooms are used, they should be set to soak for a few hours in warm water. This water should not be thrown away afterward, because it becomes particularly savory and aromatic. It should be strained and used as a condiment, either with the mushrooms or other dishes.

There are many species of mushroom that lend themselves to drying: **Amanita caesarea** 1, **rubescens** 4, **gemmata** 6, **solitaria** 10, **ovoidea** 11; **Amanitopsis (Amanita) vaginata** 12; **Agaricus campestris** 24, **silvaticus** 25, **arvensis** 26; **Clitopilus prunulus** 43; **Marasmius oreades** 48, **scorodonius** 49; **Lyophyllum Georgii** 60; **Clitocybe geotropa** 63, **gibba** 65, **nebularis** 66; **Russula aurata** 82 and all the other edible Russulas; **Boletus edulis** 111 and all the other edible Boletes; **Craterellus cornucopioides** 156; **Morchella esculenta** 170 and all the other Morels; **Mitrophora hybrida** 174; **Gyromitra esculenta** 175; **Tuber magnatum** 185, and **Tuber melanosporum** 186. Mushrooms that cannot be dried include **Coprinus comatus** 28, **atramentarius** 29; **Lactarius volemus** 74 and all the other edible **Lactarii**; **Cantharellus cibarius** 153 and all other species of tough, leathery, and corky mushrooms. Nevertheless the **Lactarius piperatus** 81 and **Lactarius vellereus** 80 are dried in some regions.

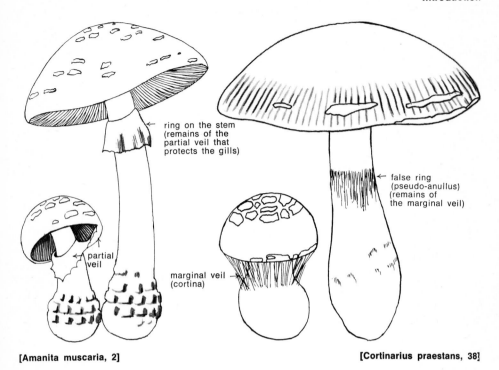

ring on the stem
(remains of the
partial veil that
protects the gills)

false ring
(pseudo-anullus)
(remains of
the marginal veil)

partial
veil

marginal veil
(cortina)

[Amanita muscaria, 2]

[Cortinarius praestans, 38]

b) Mushroom Powder

When the mushrooms are perfectly dry, they can easily be powdered. Any small electric grinder, a small coffee-grinder, for example, may be used. Powdered mushroom should be kept airtight in plastic bags or glass jars. Mushroom powder can be used as a seasoning, according to taste. Mushroom powder is prized in proportion to the aromatic properties of the mushroom from which it has been prepared.

All edible mushrooms may be dried and then powdered. The powder of **Lactarius piperatus** 81 must be kept separate from the powder of other species of mushroom, because it is particularly peppery in taste; it should be used in small quantities.

c) Mushrooms Preserved in Olive Oil

When it is impossible to dry mushrooms, for lack of time or space, or because of rainy weather, and one still wants to preserve them, they can be put up in olive oil, provided the specimens are not too mature. Clean the mushrooms, slice in large pieces, boil for two or three minutes and drain. In another pot boil vinegar, whole small onions, salt, peppercorns, bay leaf, and a sprig of rosemary for about ten minutes. Add the drained, parboiled mushrooms to the vinegar mixture and boil gently for fifteen to twenty minutes. Transfer the mushrooms to sterilized glass jars, cover to an inch above the top of the mushrooms with olive oil, and seal the jars hermetically.

Many species of mushroom can be preserved in this fashion. The principal ones are **Amanita caesarea** 1, **rubescens** 4, **gemmata** 6, **solitaria** 10, **ovoidea** 11; **Amanitopsis (Amanita) vaginata** 12; **Pholiota (Agrocybe) aegerita** 32; **Tricholoma flavovirens** 52; **Lepista nuda** 58; **Armillariella imperialis** 62; **Lactarius deliciosus** 75; **Russula aurata** 82 and all the edible **Russulae**; **Boletus edulis** 111, **aereus** 114, **pinicola** 118; **Cantharellus cibarius** 153; and **Craterellus cornucopioides** 156.

d) Mushroom Extract

Mushroom extract is prepared chiefly when there is a great quantity of mushrooms and no way to preserve them in any other fashion. The mushrooms should be set to cook without any seasoning. The juice excreted during the cooking should be poured off from the pot, and a slightly larger amount of hot water should be poured over the mushrooms. This process should be repeated several times until the mushrooms cease to secrete their fairly savory and aromatic juice. When the mushrooms have stopped secreting this juice, they should be thrown away. The juice should be kept over a flame until it becomes syrupy in consistency. Mushroom extract is a fine seasoning for rice, pasta, and meat. All mushrooms, even those that are very hard, can be used in the preparation of mushroom extract.

Cooking mushrooms

a) Cleaning

Whether you intend to serve the mushrooms at once or preserve them, they should be cleaned, not washed. Washing should be avoided unless it is absolutely necessary. Mushrooms often lose much of their aroma in washing, and a mushroom without aroma is worthless. Unfortunately, some fungi cannot be completely cleaned without using water. In such cases cold water should be used, never hot water. They should be washed quickly and dried immediately, preferably with a dry absorbent towel. But whenever one can do without washing them, one should. A well-sharpened knife, a moderately firm brush, and a sponge or an absorbent towel are enough to clean many species of mushroom.

The stems should be thrown away if they remain unchewable after cooking. Sometimes it is enough to discard the base, which is too often spongy or spoiled. Rings, volvas, and cap scales are generally insipid and sometimes indigestible; they should be removed from mushrooms that are to be eaten.

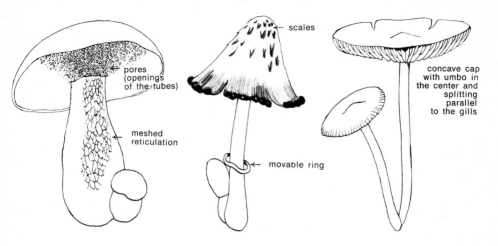

scales

pores
(openings
of the tubes)

concave cap
with umbo in
the center and
splitting
parallel
to the gills

meshed
reticulation

movable ring

The cap cuticle should also be removed if it is too tough or too sticky. Otherwise it should be kept, because the cuticle and the mushroom flesh in immediate contact with the cuticle often contain a considerable amount of the aromatic substance of the mushroom. When the gills and tubes are flaccid, they may be hard to digest and should be thrown away. Otherwise they should be left, because they often constitute the most nourishing part of the mushroom. Then there are mushrooms, as **Morchella esculenta** 170, for example, that have hollows and pits on the outer surface and are more or less hollow inside. These pits and cavities may contain insect nests or bits of totally inedible matter, including earth, sand, tiny pebbles, and bits of wood. They should be cut open and thoroughly cleaned.

b) Parboiling

It has been suggested that one not wash mushrooms even if one cannot clean them thoroughly otherwise. Sometimes, however, mushrooms require not only washing but parboiling for two or three minutes before they can be seasoned and cooked for eating. This procedure must be followed with all those mushrooms that contain bitter or sharp resins or any other harmful or unpleasant substance. This can be done easily if the cleaned and sliced mushroom are put in a large strainer and then put in boiling water. The water used for parboiling should be thrown away. It should not even be used in the preparation of feed to fatten animals.

When parboiling is necessary or even advisable, special notice is taken in the catalogue entry under the heading concerning the mushroom's edibility.

c) Warnings

Unless there are reasons to the contrary, never put a lid on the receptacle in which mushrooms are cooked until they are free of most of the water contained in their own cells. But when they have been cooking long enough, a close-fitting lid should be put on the pot so that the mushroom aroma is not lost. For this reason, it is sometimes preferable to cook mushrooms in the oven.

There are many ways to prepare mushrooms. Some of the easier recipes are given below. Every housewife and every chef may vary the recipes to suit his own taste. Nevertheless is it worth warning against the not uncommon mistake of cooking mushrooms with too many onions, too much garlic, or too much tomato paste or fresh tomato. All of these items, as well as many others, are so distinctive in taste or so strongly aromatic that they often obliterate the aroma of the mushrooms. If you want mushrooms to keep their aroma when used with rice, pasta, and meat, make sure you do not overwhelm them with these items. This is the rule, but like any other rule - and especially in matters of taste - it has its notable exceptions.

When describing a mushroom's edibility, mention is made if a certain recipe is not suited to the particular mushroom. For example, in the entry for **Lactarius deliciosus** 75, it is noted that this mushroom is good but that it should not be cooked in liquid, for it will turn into an unappetizing mush.

Recipes

Mushrooms fried in olive oil　Slice the mushrooms. Dip them in beaten egg and then in a mixture of bread crumbs and finely grated cheese. Fry them in very hot olive oil; they brown at once. Serve them with a wedge of lemon. They can be eaten as a separate course or as a side dish with roast meat. Do not forget to use salt in this recipe and in those that follow, even if it is not specifically mentioned.

Pan-fried mushrooms　Brown sliced onions in bacon fat. Then add chunks of chopped mushroom. Salt as required. Cook the mushrooms over medium heat, stirring occasionally, for about twenty minutes. Before serving, sprinkle with chopped parsley.

Mushrooms with tomato paste　Heat equal amounts of butter and olive oil and some chopped onion in a saucepan over medium heat. When onion is soft, add cleaned and thin-sliced mushrooms. Let cook for five minutes, then add diluted tomato paste and salt and pepper to taste. Allow to cook about half an hour. Before removing from the flame sprinkle with chopped parsley.

Mushrooms cooked in a saucepan　Put sliced mushrooms into a saucepan with equal amounts of butter and olive oil, a little pepper, and sufficient salt. Cook over a high flame at first, then reduce the heat to low. Toward

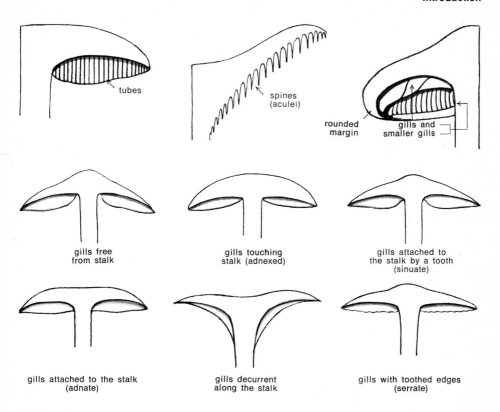

tubes

spines
(aculei)

rounded
margin

gills and
smaller gills

gills free
from stalk

gills touching
stalk (adnexed)

gills attached to
the stalk by a tooth
(sinuate)

gills attached to the stalk
(adnate)

gills decurrent
along the stalk

gills with toothed edges
(serrate)

the end, a bit of dry white wine may be added. A few minutes before serving the mushrooms, but while they are still cooking, sprinkle in parsley and a bit of chopped garlic. The mushrooms should be served very hot. Any mushroom that is not tough or fibrous may be cooked in this manner.

Mushrooms with eggs Scramble some eggs in an oven-proof pan with butter and a little salt. Cover them with mushrooms prepared according to the preceding recipe but not quite fully cooked. Sprinkle with bread-crumbs and finely grated cheese. Bake in a moderate oven until the mush-rooms are done and the cheese browned; this should require only a few minutes.

Stewed mushrooms Cook mushrooms with equal amounts of butter and olive oil, a little pepper, salt, parsley, and crushed garlic if desired. As the mushrooms begin to dry in cooking, add broth, meat sauce or meat extract diluted in warm water. The mushrooms should be cut in thickish slices, up to half an inch in thickness.

English stewed mushrooms   Soak mushrooms sliced in half, or cut up into several sections if the mushrooms are large, in water with a bit of lemon juice for a half hour or so. Remove by handfuls to free them of any sediment, and put them in a pan with melted butter. Season with salt, pepper, and a bit of lemon juice. Cook over a low flame for twenty or thirty minutes. They should be covered with a lid. Add a bit of flour and stir until it absorbs the butter. Cook for a minute then add cream or milk, stirring until it has a creamy consistency. Sprinkle lightly with freshly-grated nutmeg. Cook over moderate heat until the mushrooms are tender. Skim off excess butter, if necessary, and serve hot.

Mushrooms with squash   Brown sliced onions in oil and butter. Add small pieces of mushroom and thin strips of squash, a bit of milk and salt. Cook over low heat for about twenty minutes. This recipe is popular in Germany.

Mushrooms and cabbage   Brown sliced onions in bacon fat. Add chunks of cabbage, and mushroom, sliced or diced potatoes, and salt. Cover and cook over low heat. Remove the lid only occasionally to add water. This recipe is popular in Germany.

Stuffed mushrooms   Mushroom caps can be hollowed out and filled with a stuffing made of chopped mushroom stem, a bit of pepper, salt, parsley, breadcrumbs, and olive oil. They should be dotted with bits of butter. The mushrooms should be cooked in a hot oven in a buttered pan. They cook in less than half an hour. Meat may also be added. The following mushrooms can be used in this recipe: **Amanita caesarea** 1, **rubescens** 4, **solitaria** 10, **ovoidea** 11; **Lepiota procera** 13; **Agaricus campestris** 24, **silvaticus** 25, **arvensis** 26; **Boletus edulis** 111, **aereus** 114, **cyanescens** 117, and **pinicola** 118.

Mushroom fondue   Grease a pan with butter. Spread large thick slices of good mushroom over the pan; salt lightly. Put slices of soft cheese on the mushrooms. Make several layers of mushroom and cheese. Bake in a slow oven so that the cheese melts. If the oven is too hot, the cheese will clot. When the mushrooms are half cooked pour cream or milk over them. When the surface is golden brown, the fondue is ready to serve. It should be served very hot. Good fondue requires no other ingredients - no spices, no parsley, no onions, no garlic, and no wine.

Spaghetti with mushrooms   Cook the spaghetti as you normally would in salted water. Drain. Cook chicken or turkey giblets in equal amounts of olive oil and butter together with chopped onion. Note that the liver should be added later or it will become tough. In equal portions of olive oil and butter brown finely chopped mushrooms. Do not chop the mushrooms in a blender or they will lose much of their aroma. Put a layer of spaghetti in a casserole, then a layer of mushrooms, then a layer of spaghetti, a layer of giblets, and so on, making sure that the top layer is mushroom. Bake in a hot oven to heat through.

Gratin potatoes with mushrooms Boil unpeeled potatoes in salted water. Drain, peel, and cut them in slices; work quickly so that they do not become too cool. Arrange a layer of potato slices in a baking dish, with mushroom powder or finely chopped mushroom, fine breadcrumbs, and bits of butter. Salt. Continue with equal layers, ending with butter bits. Sprinkle grated cheese over the top. Bake in a moderate oven until the surface is lightly browned.

Mushroom balls Cut the mushrooms into small cubes. Cook them in equal amounts of butter and olive oil with salt and a bit of pepper. Knead them together with eggs, chopped cooked meat, chopped sausage, fine breadcrumbs, a bit of flour, and a bit of broth. Roll this mixture into balls. Roll the balls in beaten egg and fine breadcrumbs. Fry them in hot olive oil.

Mushroom soup Cook mushrooms and chopped onions seasoned with salt, pepper, garlic, and parsley in equal parts of butter and olive oil in a large pot. Then pour meat or vegetable broth over the mushrooms until the soup has the desired consistency. Finish cooking over a low flame. It can be served with small pieces of toast. Sprinkle over grated cheese to taste. **Lactarius deliciosus** 75 and the other edible **Lactarii** cannot be used in mushroom soup because they turn mushy as soon as they are heated in liquid.

Mushroom soup with egg Cook cut mushrooms in a pot with butter for ten minutes. Pour broth over them and cook for another ten minutes. Add salt, perhaps some dry white wine, and thicken with egg yolks.

Mushrooms in cream Place well-cleaned mushrooms in a baking dish. Sprinkle with salt and pepper. Add a bit of butter and cover the mushrooms with cream or milk. Cover securely. Place in a hot oven and bake for twenty minutes. Remove the lid of the pan only when ready to serve.

Creamed mushrooms Remove the stalk and cap margin from the mushrooms. Melt butter or margarine in a saucepan and add a bit of flour. Cook this mixture slowly, stirring with a wooden spoon. Push the mixture up around the sides of the saucepan and pour cold milk into the middle, stirring well until thoroughly incorporated and smooth. Bring it to a boil and add the mushrooms. Cook for twenty-five minutes over low heat, stirring often. Add salt and a bit of pepper. Serve on toast, sprinked with parsley.

Cream of mushrooms Cook the mushrooms with a bit of butter and a large amount of broth, preferably chicken, over medium heat for twenty minutes. In another pan, cook equal amounts of butter and flour, stirring for 3 minutes. Dilute the mixture with milk and cook until it becomes creamy. Add the mushrooms and broth and season with salt and pepper. Cook for another few minutes, stirring until the mixture in smooth and creamy.

Purée of mushrooms Purée cream of mushrooms, prepared according to the preceding recipe, in a blender or food mill.

Boy Scout mushrooms Make a skewer from a straight branch, skewer mushrooms and roast them over burning embers that have stopped smoking. Pour melted butter over the mushrooms and sprinkle with salt and pepper. All tender edible mushrooms can be prepared this way, except for Morels and similar species.

Hungarian recipe Fry sliced mushrooms in butter with salt, pepper, and paprika. Add a bit of any hot sauce and cook another five minutes over medium heat.

Greek recipe Marinate the mushrooms in oil and white vinegar for about ten hours together with salt, pepper, parsley, onion, and chopped garlic. Then cook the mushrooms. Let them cool. Add lemon juice and serve as hors d'oeuvre.

Marinated mushrooms Liberally salt medium-sized mushrooms, mix them well, and leave them in salt for a day or two. Carefully drain the fluid exuded by the mushrooms and sprinkle them with mustard seed, ground clove, powdered ginger, black pepper, and pickling spice. Heat them just until the boiling point is reached. Then remove them from the heat and let them soak in the refrigerator, tightly covered, for two weeks. Remove the fluid that has been produced again by the mushrooms, and they are ready to serve. They can be used as a side dish. This recipe is popular in England.

Spanish recipe Fry some onions, green pepper, and garlic cloves in butter. Add mushrooms cut into small pieces and cook for two minutes. Add strained boiled tomatoes, salt, and pepper. Cook for another hour over medium heat. Mushrooms prepared in this manner are good served with chicken.

Lamb with mushrooms Roll lean pieces of lamb in flour and brown in butter. Add chopped onion and a bit of dry white wine. Cook over a low flame until meat is tender and almost done. Roll small pieces of mushroom in flour and fry in butter. Add a bit of any hot sauce and cook until mushrooms are done. Serve the lamb with mushroom garnish on the side.

Mushroom salad   Season sliced mushrooms with salt, olive oil, and lemon juice. Parsley and pepper may be added to taste. Garlic is not recommended. One should serve only half-matured mushrooms in this manner.
The following mushrooms may be served this way: **Amanita caesarea** 1, **Lepiota procera** 13, **Agaricus campestris** 24, **Agaricus silvaticus** 25, **Agaricus arvensis** 26, **Boletus edulis** 111, **Boletus aereus** 114, **Boletus pinicola** 118, **Lycoperdon maximum** 160, **Lycoperdon bovista** 161, **Fistulina hepatica** 142.
Watery or very aromatic mushrooms should be left to sit for a few hours seasoned only with salt so they will lose much of the water they contain or a bit of their aroma. The water exuded by the mushrooms should be thrown out, and then the mushrooms can be seasoned with olive oil and lemon juice.

Lepiota steaks   Scrape the harder scales off the mushroom caps, and use only slightly mature mushrooms. Pour hot melted butter over them. Sprinkle with salt and a bit of pepper. Cook them for a few seconds under a hot broiler, making sure that the gills are facing upward. Turn them quickly and broil just a few seconds more. Serve at once.

Sautéed meadow mushrooms   Remove the stalks, which may be cooked separately in any manner. Arrange the caps, whole or sliced, in a saucepan. Pour melted butter over them and salt. Cover the saucepan with a tight-fitting lid and cook over a very low flame for twenty minutes. Mix a bit of flour in cold milk until smooth, then add more milk, and pour it all over the mushrooms. Sprinkle with white pepper. Boil for a few minutes, stirring well.

Meadow mushrooms or chanterelles with liver   Fry chicken or veal liver slices in butter together with lean ham and chopped onion. Remove from the heat just as the onions begin to brown. Fry small pieces of mushroom in another pan and then put them on the fried liver. Sprinkle with pepper and salt.

Buttered mushrooms   Slice mushrooms, roll them in flour, add salt, and fry in butter over a high flame. Serve them piping hot.

Mushroom Hors d'oeuvre   Beat together olive oil, lemon juice, a pinch of pepper, salt and chopped aromatic herbs. Add a clove of garlic. Let this mixture sit for an hour. Remove the garlic and immerse sliced mushrooms. Leave them for an hour, then remove them, drain carefully, and serve raw as hors d'oeuvre.

Fried Coprini   Cut the **Coprini** in half lengthwise. Fry them over a high flame with a bit of butter and salt. While they are frying, shake the pan but do not mix with a spoon or fork or the mushrooms will break. Once the butter starts to boil, lower the flame and cover the pan; they should cook for another five minutes over low heat. **Coprinus comatus** 28 is very delicate and easily digested when prepared this way.

Japanese-style Armillaria In Japan the **Armillaria Matzutake** is used in this recipe; elsewhere **Armillariella (Armillaria) mellea** 61 or even **Cantharellus cibarius** 153 and some very young Polypores can be used. The mushrooms should be cut into thin slices. Veal, pork, or chicken should be cut into thin slices. The meat and mushrooms should be placed in the center of a large frying pan. Around them, in three separate piles, should be arranged celery, scallions or small fresh onions, and green peppers. Pour soy sauce and a bit of saki or strong dry white wine over. Cook covered. Serve in spoonfuls around dry cooked rice.

Oyster-style Pleurotus ostreatus Cut the tender caps from clusters of **Pleurotus ostreatus** 69, and discard the rest. Dip the oyster-shaped caps in beaten egg, roll in breadcrumbs, and add salt and pepper. Then fry in equal amounts of olive oil and butter over a very high flame. They are served piping hot.

Lactarius mush Stewed **Lactarii** usually dissolve in the pan. But there are some people who like them this way. They should be sliced, salted, and cooked over a low flame for about an hour in a bit of broth. Then a bit of butter should be melted and flour added. Mix well and then add the mushrooms. Bring to a boil, stirring well. Toward the end, chopped aromatic herbs and a bit of pepper should be added.

Sautéed Boletes Use moderately developed mushrooms with very immature tubes. Otherwise the tubes and part of the stalk should be removed. Cut into small pieces. Cook in butter in a covered pan for twenty minutes over low heat. Sprinkle over and stir in a bit of flour, add some broth, and cook for another ten minutes.

Provençal Boletes Fry the mushrooms in peanut oil for fiifteen minutes with salt and pepper. Add a few cloves of crushed garlic and cook for five minutes more. Then add a bit of vinegar and cook for another five minutes.

Toulouse-style Boletes Follow the recipe for **Provençal Boletes**, but add small onions, ham, and tomato when you add the garlic.

Hydna with sherry Boil **Hydnum (Dentinum) repandum** 144 for one minute. Throw out the water from this parboiling. Cook the mushrooms in a covered saucepan for twenty minutes with butter, salt, pepper, and a bit of milk or good broth. If you use milk, make sure that the heat is very low, otherwise the milk will scorch. Add a bit of sherry at the last minute and serve hot over toast.

Chanterelles with eggplant   Fry sliced eggplant in oil. Remove the eggplant from the pan and drain. Fry small onions and sliced green pepper in butter. Roll pieces of **Chanterelle** 153 in flour. Add to the chanterelles the eggplant, onions, peppers, cooked tomatoes, salt, pepper, and aromatic herbs. Bake in a moderate oven for twenty minutes.

Chanterelles with eggs   Roll small pieces of chanterelle in flour. Cook in butter over a high flame. Pour beaten egg over the mushrooms. Add a bit of pepper, salt, and a pinch of aromatic herbs. Cook until the eggs are set to taste. Serve immediately.

Chanterelles with ham   Cut the mushrooms into small pieces and liberally sprinkle with flour. Fry them in butter with a few slices of onion. Add chunks of ham and a bit of hot sauce. Cook over moderate heat, without boiling, until the mushrooms are tender. Sprinkle with chopped parsley and a bit of pepper.

Fried Puffballs   Do not mistake Puffballs for immature poisonous **Amanitae** 2, 3, 7, 8, or 9. When in doubt cut the mushrooms in half. If they are **Amanitae** you will see the stalk and cap in section. Remove the outer covering of the Puffballs, cut in thick slices, sprinkle with flour, and fry quickly in butter. Season with salt and very little pepper.
The following Puffballs may be used in this recipe: **maximum** 160, **bovista** 161, and **perlatum** 162.

Stuffed Morels   Slice the mushrooms in half lengthwise, sprinkle with flour, and stuff with chopped chicken livers mixed with fine breadcrumbs and egg yolk. Sprinkle chopped onion over them and add a bit of pepper. Bake in a moderate oven for fifteen minutes.
The following Morels may be used in this recipe: **esculenta** 170, **deliciosa** 172, **vulgaris** 171, and **conica** 173.

WARNING

Precautions

The prudence and care taken by mycologists when describing the edibility of mushrooms in the works they address to the public is beyond criticism. There are, sometimes, differing views among various authors as to the edibility of certain mushrooms. But as soon as there is the slightest doubt about a particular species, it is immediately characterized as suspect and automatically excluded from the list of edible mushrooms.

So accidents with mushrooms cannot be attributed to the mycologist but rather to other reasons. First, mushrooms do, of course, cause poisoning - and in spite of this people continue to eat them without descretion, often relying on totally false tests for edibility. This is more true in Europe, where wild mushrooms are prized as food, than in the U.S., where many people flee all wild mushrooms with superstitious fear.

But even among that small group which uses the existing guides there is often a negligent attitude. Many are often too confident that they have found a particular species of mushroom, otherwise new to them, and that they are certain of its edibility. That is why in this guide's descriptions frequent reference is made to the possibility of confusing one particular species with another. At times the most striking distinction between an edible and a poisonous mushroom will depend on a single common, visible detail - for example the way in which the gills join the stalk.

Yet, even when the mushrooms one picks are among those species listed as edible, if the specimens are too mature, or are wormy, or spoiled, they can be harmful - just like meat that has spoiled. Many accidents believed to be caused by poisonous mushrooms are actually due to edible, even excellent, yet spoiled specimens.

So it should always be kept in mind that when a mushroom is described as **edible good excellent** this description always presupposes: **not too mature**, **in good condition**, and **properly cooked**. In special instances these details will be explicitly stated and emphasized.

There are some precautions to take when collecting mushrooms for the table that will help avoid the possibility of mushroom poisoning.

1 Never eat any mushroom you have not identified with absolute certainty. There are thousands of fungi, and no complete single guide available. Most are unimportant as food.

2 Familiarize yourself thoroughly with the characteristics of the **Amantinae**. A beginner should scrupulously avoid all Amanitas, even those listed as edible, because of the possibility of a **deadly mistake**.

3 Always wash hands thoroughly after handling any poisonous Amanita that has been picked for identification. The spores are poisonous also. Do not place Amanitas in the same container with mushrooms that are identified as edible and collected for eating.

4 Keep in mind that some mushrooms are edible for some people and poisonous for others. Some mushrooms in this guide are so designated. If such a mushroom is to be tried, eat just a very small amount at the first tasting and wait for several hours to see if there is any adverse reactions.

5 When trying a mushroom for the first time, eat in small quantities. There is always the possibility of a particular mushroom not agreeing with a certain person, even if it is consistently reported as edible and choice.

6 If you tend to be allergic to foods or pollens, be exceptionally careful when trying new species. It would seem advisable to avoid those that report differing reactions for different people.

7 Cut all small puffballs in half to avoid the deadly possibility of mistakenly picking an Amanita in the button stage.

8 To Repeat: **Never eat any mushroom you have not identified with absolute certainty**.

About mushroom poisoning

The most serious mushroom poisonings occur from ingestion of poisonous Amanitas. Those related to the **A. muscaria** 2 group, which contain muscarin, will produce symptoms within 2-3 hours, including sweating, vomiting, cramps, diarrhea and effects similar to some hallucinogenic drugs. These Amanitas can and do lead to coma and death, although usually only when eaten in quantity. Atropine is a specific for muscarin-related poisoning (also for **Clitocybe olearia** 64) and should be administed by a physician in doses of 1 mg. every 1-2 hours until the situation is under control.
Poisoning from Amanitas related to **A. phalloides** 7, such as **A. verna** 8 and **A. virosa** 9 is much more serious, and some place the death rate from these phalloidine-containing fungi as high as 70 per cent. Symptoms occur

usually from 6 to 15 hours after ingestion, at which time there is a dramatic onset of nausea, vomiting and diarrhea accompanied by severe pain. The poison attacks the heart muscles, kidney and liver, with jauntice following in 2-3 days. Death occurs in 5 to 8 days. Even if a person survives, permanent damage may be done. There is no positive antidote for such mushroom poisoning, although medication and a high-carbohydrate diet are indicated to prevent severe liver damage. It should be noted here that rabbits do not succumb to **A. phalloides** poisoning, and some success has been reported in Europe treating affected persons with finely chopped, uncooked rabbit brain and stomach. Reports also indicate some success with a French antidote.

Luckily, most mushrooms listed as poisonous are not deadly, although some produce very severe symptoms. In most cases victims of mushroom poisoning are left with no more than an uncomfortable memory - with all symptoms disappearing in a day or two.

Some general information:

1 The best cure is prevention - never eat a mushroom you have not been able to identify positively. Take the precautions outlined in the previous section.

2 Do not attempt home remedies when mushroom poisoning is suspected - valuable time may be lost. Call a doctor immediately or go to the emergency ward of the nearest hospital. An attempt can be made to induce vomiting, but without the aid of medication.

3 If at all possible, bring a specimen mushroom with you. In lieu of any, and if vomiting occurs, it is essential to retain any non-digested pieces which might help to identify the mushroom.

4 Any unexplained stomach pains, nausea or cramps that occur suddenly within 24 hours after eating gilled mushrooms should be immediately suspected of being phalloidine poisoning and the victim taken to the hospital - the onset of symptoms has been known to take this long.

5 If you tend to be allergic to certain foods, or have hay fever or other allergies, be cautions with **all** mushrooms. Avoid particularly those fungi listed as **Suspect**, and take the usual precautions listed in the previous section.

NAMING MUSHROOMS

An amateur "mushroom hunter" (as opposed to a professional "mycologist") is usually faced with two major problems - first, the inability to identify many of the mushrooms he finds (because no single illustrated guide exists - there are thousands of fungi) and second, the bewildering fact that sometimes seemingly identical mushrooms pictured and described in various guidebooks have different names.

It is not generally known by mushroom hunters interested primarily in delicacies for the table that the naming of mushrooms is governed by an International Code of Botanical Nomenclature, which is revised when necessary at International Botanical Congress meetings. This Code defines precisely how botanical names may or may not be used, built up from the binomial (two-name) system proposed by Linnaeus in 1753, in which all plants are given first a generic name (for all members of a group or genus that possess common characteristics) followed by a specific epithet (to distinguish one of the group, or a species of the genus). That is, for the deadly **Amanita verna** 8, **Amanita** is the generic (genus) name, and **verna**, is the specific (species) epithet that sets this mushroom apart from all other mushrooms bearing the genus name **Amanita**.

The names applied to mushrooms are taken from Greek or Latin, or treated as such, in the recognized universal language of science.

For fungi, the International Code uses as a starting point the classifications and names in Elias Fries' Systema Mycologicum, Volume One (covering mushrooms, 1821) and Volume Two (the Discomycetes, [1] 1822), and for the fungi not covered by Fries, Persoon's Synopsis Methodica Fungorum (Puffballs, rusts and smuts, 1801) was adopted. This point represents the **first use** of a specific name which is therefore automatically valid. Further Code rules govern, among other things, the naming of species unknown to either Fries or Persoon, as well as changes that occur because of reclassification of a fungi.

Changes in the Latin names for mushrooms occur for various reasons and

---

[1] Fungi that are variously clubshaped, cup- or disc-shaped, sometimes convoluted and in which the method of producing spores are similar, such as **Morchellae**, **Pezizae** and **Helvellae**.

sometimes, as in the case of the Giant Puffball [2] with great frequency - the Code does not control the movement of a mushroom from one genus to another, it only controls what the mushroom will be called when it gets there.

If two species classified in the same genus are found to be identical, but sport different specific names, the first one applied, the earliest, is valid - the earliest, of course, being assigned from Persoon for Puffballs, and Fries for all the rest of the mushrooms except those discovered and classified after the publication of their names. The later name becomes a synonym for the earlier. For the mushroom hunter it is perhaps more apt to call it an alias - for if published alone in a mushroom guide it hides the correct name from him quite effectively - unlike the mycologist, he is likely to accept it automatically as valid. The Code cannot prevent mistakes in nomenclature from being made, it can only dictate what must be done when the mistake is discovered.

When two different species are found to have the same name in the same genus, the later species epithet must be changed, as it is not valid; that is, it must assume a name of its own. The Code does not control classification, it can only control the names used in the classification.

A more elaborate situation occurs when a mushroom that had not been previously know is named - and it is incorrectly classified by genus. Along comes a different mycologist who finds and classifies the same mushroom, naming it in its proper genus and assigning it his choice of species epithet. When the duplication is eventually discovered, perhaps by yet another mycologist, a "new combination" must be formed, merging the valid genus name (as classified by the second mycologist) with the valid species epithet (that of the first mycologist).

New names are covered by Code regulations, as well as situations where certain names are "preserved" and used even though they would normally fall outside the structure of the Code. A copy of **The International Code of Botanical Nomenclature** can be found in any library.

The changing of names and growing lists of synonyms resulting from reclassification of fungi (usually determined by laboratory research - such as chemical and miscroscopic examination - intermixed with individual educated guesses) is further complicated for the mushroom hunter by the fact that even new guidebooks for the amateur often retain nomenclature considered no longer accurate by professional mycologists.

It is, therefore, good to be aware of the fact that, as Gertrude Stein said, a rose is a rose is a rose. A change in nomenclature, either of the genus

---

[2] In 1949, A. H. Smith listed the following scientific names for the Giant Puffball in his Mushrooms in their Natural Habitats (without his citations): **Calvatia gigantea, Lycoperdon giganteum, Bovista gigantea, Lycoperdon Bovista, Calvatia maxima, Calvatia Bovista, Calvatia primitiva.**

or species name, in no way alters the edibility of or the features by which a person identifying a mushroom for food will rely in the field. There are good, valid reasons for an amateur to be aware of, and to understand how and why the scientific (Latin) names of mushrooms change, but no matter how many times the Giant Puffball changes names, it still remains the Giant Puffball and very edible.

There is another part to nomenclature, though, that is designed to help the situation. That is, mycologists do not consider a mushroom properly named unless the authors of the name are cited. If the book in which the citation appears is using abbreviations for mycologists' name, this takes the form of an undecipherable series of letters, periods and parenthesis the key to which the mushroom hunter soon realizes is not in the book. Rules set down by the Code also cover the citing of authorities, and it is not only easy to decipher when explained, but extremely interesting, as well. For the citing of the authors gives a history of the change in the status of mushrooms, or at the very least indicates that the first citing of the name still stands.

The best way to explain the citing procedure is with examples. The easiest citation is one such as **Hydnum imbricatum Fries**. It means, simply, that the mushroom in question was named by Fries and that it remains the correct name for this mushroom. The same is true if Fries had been abbreviated, of course. A good example is mushroom 97 in this volume, which properly cited would read **Hygrophorus russula (Schaeff. ex Fr.) Quél**. This is not as complicated as it looks if one keeps in mind that the earliest specific epithet is not changeable. So, the (**Schaef. ex Fr.**) means that Fries accepted the name for the mushroom in question given it by J. C. Schaeffer, and by accepting this name he validated it, as Fries is automatically the first use of the name according to the Code. But the citation continues - (**Schaeffer. ex Fr.) Quél**. What has happened here is that Quélet came along later, took a look at Fries' mushroom and decided that Fries had placed it in the wrong genus (Fries classified practically all of the gilled mushrooms as **Agaricae**). It was, he decided, a **Hygrophorus** - and so he reclassifed is as such, bringing along with the mushroom the specific epithet **russula**, which remains valid. But there is some disagreement here, for the mushroom also supports **Limacium russula (Schaeff. ex Fr.) Ricken**. In this case, the mushroom named by Schaeffer and validated by Fries was examined by A. Ricken, who promptly reclassified it as belonging to the genus **Limacium** retaining, of course, the valid specific name. **Hygrophorus russula** and **Limacium russula** are, of course, synonyms, and neither is more correct than the other - in terms of the classification of each mycologist. Other mycologists, however, are perfectly free to choose which genus classification they believe to be more accurate.

One more example, a bit more complicated. The mushroom numbered 83 is usually cited **Russula emetica (Schaeff. ex Fr.) Pers. ex S. F. Gray**. In one sentence: the mushroom named by Schaeffer and validated by Fries was moved with its specific epithet to the genus Russula, where it was validated by S. F. Gray.

So, citations inside parenthesis refer to the species, and those outside the parenthesis refer to the genus. Such citations help the amateur evaluate genus changes, and are particularly helpful when a new genus name crops up in a guidebook attributed to an active mycologist. The new genus name is representative of the most modern thinking on the mushrooms in question, and it provides the mushroom hunter with an available source of additional information, for it is obvious that the nomenclature adopted in the newest taxonomic classification is apt to be preferred by most mycologists.

NOMENCLATURE

The American edition of this book has made some changes from the original in the following nomenclature:

1 In each instance the genus and species name followed by a single-name citation in parenthesis is the name and citation assigned by Dr. von Frieden. Fuller citations have been added in most cases.

2 A name in **bold face** type is accepted. If it replaces the author's name, it will be followed by a complete citation.

3 A second bold face name is added to update the book whenever the name is either a more widely-known synonym or a name characteristic of more modern classification. Either is correct, but the second is generally preferred.

4 A genus name in brackets, as [Psalliota] is incorrect for reasons of nomenclature.

5 Additional entries are either as provided by Dr. von Frieden, or added to aid the user in the United States.

1 **AMANITA CAESAREA** (Quélet)
(Scop. ex Fr.) Pers. ex Schw.
Caesar's Agaric
Excellent

2 **AMANITA MUSCARIA** (Quélet)
(L. ex Fr.) Pers. ex Hooker
Fly Agaric
Poisonous

3 **AMANITA PANTHERINA** (Quélet)
(DC. ex Fr.) Secr.
False Blusher; Panther Cap
Poisonous

4 **AMANITA RUBESCENS** (Quélet)
(Pers. ex Fr.) S. F. Gray
Blusher; Red Amanita
Excellent when cooked

5 **AMANITA CITRINA** (Roques)
(Schaeff.) ex S. F. Gray
Amanita mappa
False Death Cap
Inedible

6 **AMANITA GEMMATA**
(Fr.) Gill.
Amanita junquillea (Quélet)
Good With caution

7 **AMANITA PHALLOIDES**
(Vaill. ex Fr.) Secr.
Amanita viridis (Persoon)
Agaricus bulbosus
Death Cap
Deadly

8 **AMANITA VERNA** (Gillet)
(Bull. ex Fr.) Pers. ex Vitt.
Destroying Angel
Deadly

9 **AMANITA VIROSA** (Quélet)
Secr.
Destroying Angel
Deadly

10 **AMANITA SOLATARIA** (Secretan)
(Bull. ex Fr.) Secr.
Woodland Amanita
Edible

11 **AMANITA OVOIDEA** (Quélet)
Good

12 **AMANITOPSIS VAGINATA** (Roze)
AMANITA VAGINATA
(Bull. ex Fr.) Vitt.
Grissette
Good

13 **LEPIOTA PROCERA** (Quélet)
(Scop. ex Fr.) S. F. Gray
MACROLEPIOTA PROCERA
(Scop. ex Fr.) Singer
Parasol Mushroom
Excellent

14 **LEPIOTA RHACODES** (Quélet)
(Vitt.) Quél.
MACROLEPIOTA RHACODES
(Vitt.) Singer
Shaggy Lepiota
Excellent

15 **LEPIOTA EXCORIATA** (Quélet)
(Schaeff. ex Fr.) Kumm.
Flaky Agaric
Excellent

16 **LEPIOTA ACUTESQUAMOSA** (Gillet)
(Weinmann) Kummer
Squarrose Agaric
Inedible

17 **LEPIOTA CRISTATA** (Quélet)
(Fr.) Kummer
Stinking Agaric
Suspect

18 **LEPIOTA HELVEOLA** (Bresadola)
Deadly

19 **LEPIOTA LEUCOTHITES**
(Vitt.) Orton
Lepiota naucina (Quélet)
White Lepiota
Good

20 **VOLVARIELLA SPECIOSA** (Fr. ex Fr.)
Singer **var. SPECIOSA**
[Volvaria] speciosa (Gillet)
Dunghil Agaric
Good

21 **VOLVARIELLA SPECIOSA** (Fr. ex Fr.)
Singer **var. GLOIOCEPHALA**
(DC. ex Fr.) Singer
[Volvaria] gloiocephala (Gillet)

Dunghil Agaric
Good

22 **VOLVARIELLA BOMBYCINA**
(Schaeff. ex Fr.) Singer
[Volvaria] bombycina (Quélet)
Silky Agaric
Good

23 **PLUTEUS CERVINUS** (Quélet)
(Schaeff. ex Fr.) Kummer
Deer Mushroom
Edible

24 **AGARICUS CAMPESTRIS**
L. ex Fr.
[Psalliota] campestris (Quélet)
Meadow Mushroom
Excellent

25 **AGARICUS SILVATICUS**
Schaeff. ex Secr.
[Psalliota] silvatica (Quélet)
Wood Agaric
Excellent

26 **AGARICUS ARVENSIS**
Schaeff. ex Secr.
[Psalliota] arvensis (Fries)
Horse Mushroom
Excellent

27 **AGARICUS XANTHODERMUS**
Genevier
[Psalliota] xanthoderma (Roze)
Yellow-Staining Mushroom
Suspect

28 **COPRINUS COMATUS** (Fries)
(Müll, ex Fr.) S. F. Gray
Shaggy Mane
Good

29 **COPRINUS ATRAMENTARIUS** (Fries)
(Bull. ex Fr.) Fr.
Inky Cap
Edible with caution

30 **HYPHOLOMA FASCICULARE** (Quélet)
NAEMATOLOMA FASCICULARE
(Huds. ex Fr.) Karst
Sulphur Tuft
Suspect

31 **HYPHOLOMA SUBLATERITIUM** (Quélet)
NAEMATOLOMA SUBLATERITIUM
(Fr.) Karst
Brick Cap
Suspect

32 **PHOLIOTA AEGERITA** (Quélet)
AGROCYBE AEGERITA
(Bolt. ex Fr.) Singer
Excellent

33 **PHOLIOTA DESTRUENS** (Fries)
Not recommended

34 **PHOLIOTA SQUARROSA** (Quélet)
(Müller. ex Fr.) Kummer
Scaly Pholiota
Edible

35 **PHOLIOTA MUTABILIS** (Quélet)
KUEHNEROMYCES MUTABILIS
(Schaeff. ex Fr.) Singer & Smith
Changeable Agaric
Good

36 **PHOLIOTA CAPERATA** (Gillet)
ROZITES CAPERATA
(Pers. ex Fr.) Karst.
Gypsy Mushroom
Good

37 **STROPHARIA AERUGINOSA** (Quélet)
(Curt ex Fr.) Quél
Green Agaric
Inedible

38 **CORTINARIUS PRAESTANS** (Saccardo)
(Cord.) Sacc.
Phlegmacium praestans
Cortinarius torvus
Good

39 **CORTINARIUS PURPURASCENS** (Fries)
Fr.
Phlegmacium purpurascens
Purplish Cortinarius
Edible

40 **CORTINARIUS FIRMUS**
Good

41 **INOCYBE PATOUILLARDII** (Bresadola)
Bres.
Red-Staining Inocybe
Poisonous

42 **ENTOLOMA LIVIDUM** (Quélet)
RHODOPHYLLUS SINUATUS
(Bull. ex Fr.) Singer
Leaden Entoloma
Poisonous

43 **CLITOPILUS PRUNULUS** (Quélet)
(Scop. ex Fr.) Kummer
Paxillus prunulus
Plum Agaric
Excellent

44 **LACCARIA LACCATA** (Berkeley &
Broome)
(Scop. ex Fr.) Cke.
Common Laccaria
Edible

45 **COLLYBIA FUSIPES** (Quélet)
Spindle-Stem
Edible with caution

46 **COLLYBIA VELUTIPES** (Quélet)
FLAMMULINA VELUTIPES
(Curt. ex Fr.) Karst.
Winter Mushroom
Good

47 **MUCIDULA MUCIDA** (Patouillard)
OUDEMANSIELLA MUCIDA
(Schrad. ex Fr.) Höhn
Clammy Agaric; Porcelain Fungus
Edible

48 **MARASMIUS OREADES** (Fries)
(Bolt. ex Fr.) Fr.
Fairy-Ring Mushroom
Excellent

49 **MARASMIUS SCORODONIUS** (Fries)
(Fr.) Fr.
Garlic Mushroom
Edible

50 **MYCENA PURA** (Quélet)
(Pers. ex Fr.) Kummer
Amethyst Agaric
Edible

51 **TRICHOLOMA PORTENTOSUM** (Quélet)
(Fr.) Quél.
Dingy Agaric
Good

52 **TRICHOLOMA FLAVOVIRENS**
(Pers. ex Fr.) Lundell
Tricholoma equestre (Quélet)
Man On Horseback
Good

53 **TRICHOLOMA SULPHREUM** (Quélet)
(Bull. ex Fr.) Kummer
Sulphury Agaric
Suspect

54 **TRICHOLOMA TERREUM** (Quélet)
(Schaeff. ex Fr.) Kummer
Gray Agaric
Good

55 **TRICHOLOMA ACERBUM** (Quélet)
Bitter Agaric
Edible

56 **TRICHOLOMA PARDINUM** (Quélet)
Quél.
Gray Tricholoma
Poisonous

57 **HEBELOMA CRUSTULINIFORME**
(Quélet)
(Bull. ex St. Amans) Quél.
Ring Agaric
Suspect

58 **LEPISTA NUDA**
(Bull. ex Fr.) Cke
Rhodopaxillus nudus (R. Maire)
Tricholoma nudum
Great Violet Rider
Good with caution

59 **MELANOLEUCA GRAMMOPODIA**
(Patouillard)
Ring Agaric
Not recommended

60 **LYOPHYLLUM GEORGII** (Singer)
Tricholoma Georgii
Calocybe Georgii
St. George's Mushroom
Excellent

61 **ARMILLARIELLA MELLEA** (Karsten)
ARMILLARIA MELLEA
(Vahl ex Fr.) Kummer
Clitocybe mellea
Honey Mushroom
Good

62 **ARMILLARIELLA IMPERIALIS**
(Konrand & Maublanc)
ARMILLARIA IMPERIALIS
Clitocybe imperialis
Edible

63 **CLITOCYBE GEOTROPA** (Quélet)
Trumpet Agaric
Good

64 **CLITOCYBE OLEARIA** (R. Marie)
Clitocybe illudens
Pleurotus olearius
Omphalotus olearius
Jack O'Lantern
Poisonous

65 **CLITOCYBE GIBBA**
(Pers. ex Fr.) Kummer
Clitocybe infundibuliformis (Quélet)
Funnel Agaric
Edible

66 **CLITOCYBE NEBULARIS** (Quélet)
(Batsch ex Fr.) Kummer
Clouded Agaric
Good

67 **CLITOCYBE DEALBATA** (Quélet)
(Sow. ex Fr.) Kummer
Clitocybe rivulosa sub. dealbata
Sweat-Producing Clitocybe
Poisonous

68 **LEPISTA INVERSA** (Patouillard)
CLITOCYBE INVERSA (Singer)
Clitocybe flaccida
Brown-Red Clitocybe
Good

69 **PLEUROTUS OSTREATUS**
(Jacquin ex Fr.) Kummer
Oyster Mushroom
Good

70 **PLEUROTUS ERYNGII** (Quélet)
Excellent

71 **PLEUROTUS FUSCUS VAR. FERULAE**
LANZI (Bresadola)
Excellent

72 **PLEUROTUS CORNUCOPIAE** (Gillet)
Good

73 **LENTINELLUS COCHLEATUS** (Karsten)
LENTINUS COCHLEATUS
(Pers. ex Fr.) Fr.
Shell Lentinus
Edible

74 **LACTARIUS VOLEMUS** (Fries)
(Fr.) Fr.
Orange-Brown Lactarius
Good

75 **LACTARIUS DELICIOSU**S (Fries)
(L. ex Fr.) S. F. Gray
Saffron Milk Cap
Good

76 **LACTARIUS TORMINOSUS** (Fries)
(Schaeff. ex Fr.) S. F. Gray
Wooly Milk Cap
Suspect

77 **LACTARIUS SCROBICULATUS** (Fries)
(Scop. ex Fr.) Fr.
Inedible

78 **LACTARIUS RUFUS** (Fries)
(Scop. ex Fr.) Fr.
Red Lactarius
Suspect

79 **LACTARIUS CONTROVERSUS**
(Pers. ex Fr.) Fr.
Stained Lactarius
Edible

80 **LACTARIUS VELLEREUS** (Fries)
(Fr.) Fr.
Wooly-White Lactarius
Edible with caution

81 **LACTERIUS PIPERATUS** (Fries)
(Scop. ex Fr.) S. F. Gray
Pepper Cap
Edible with caution

82 **RUSSULA AURATA** (Fries)
Golden Russula
Good

83 **RUSSULA EMETICA** (Fries)
(Schaeff. ex Fr.) Pers. ex S. F. Gray
Emetic Russula; The Sickener
Poisonous

84 **RUSSULA LEPIDA** (Fries)
Scaly Russula
Edible

85 **RUSSULA VESCA** (Fries)
Edible Russula
Good

86 **RUSSULA INTEGRA** (Fries)
Good

87 **RUSSULA BADIA** (Quélet)
Poisonous

88 **RUSSULA CYANOXANTHA** (Fries)
Blue-and-Yellow Russula
Good

89 **RUSSULA OLIVACEA** (Fries)
Good

90 **RUSSULA VIRESCENS** (Fries)
Greenish Russula
Good

91 **RUSSULA DELICA** (Fries)
Weaned Russula
Edible

92 **RUSSULA LUTEA** (Fries)
Yellow Russula
Excellent

93 **RUSSULA OCHROLEUCA** (Fries)
Ochrey Russula
Inedible

94 **RUSSULA FOETENS** (Fries)
(Pers. ex Fr.) Pers ex Fr.
Fetid Russula
Suspect

95 **RUSSULA ALBONIGRA** (Fries)
Scorched Russula
Edible

96 **RUSSULA NIGRICANS** (Fries)
Blackish Russula
Edible

97 **HYGROPHOROUS RUSSULA** (Quélet)
(Schaeff. ex Fr.) Quél.
Limacium russula
(Schaeff. ex Fr.) Ricken
Russula Hygrophorus
Edible

98 **HYGROPHORUS NIVEUS** (Fries)
(Scop. ex Fr.) Fr.
Camarophyllus niveus
Snow-White Hygrophorous
Good

99 **HYGROPHOROUS CHRYSODON** (Fries)
Limacium chrysodon
Yellow Downy
Good

100 **HYGROPHOROUS AGATHOSMUS** (Fries)
Limacium agathosmus
Good

101 **HYGROPHOROUS MAZUOLUS**
(Bresadola)
Camarophyllus marzuolus
Excellent

102 **HYGROPHOROUS PRATENSIS** (Fries)
CAMAROPHYLLUS PRATENSIS (Singer)
Meadow Hygrophorous
Good

103 **HYGROPHOROUS PUNICEUS** (Fries)
HYGROCYBE PUNICEA (Singer)
Good

104 **HYGROPHOROUS AURANTIACA**
(R. Marie)
Clitocybe aurantiaca
(Wulf. ex Fr.) Studer
Cantharellus aurantiacus
False Chanterelle
Good with caution

105 **PAXILLUS INVOLUTUS** (Fries)
(Batsch ex Fr.) Fr.
Involute Paxillus
Good with caution

106 **GOMPHIDIUS RUTILUS**
(Schaeff. ex Fr.) Lundell
Gomphidius viscidus (Fries)
Viscid Gomphidius
Good

107 **GOMPHIDIUS GLUTINOSUS** (Fries)
(Schaeff. ex Fr.) Fr.
Glutinous Gomphidius
Good

108 **STROBILOMYCES FLOCCOPUS**
(Vahl ex Fr.) Karst.
Strobilomyces strobilaceus (Berkeley)
Pine Cone Mishroom
Not recommended

109 **BOLETUS AURANTIACUS** (Bulliard)
LECCINUM AURANTIACUM
(Bull. ex St. Amans) S. F. Gray
Boletus scaber var. aurantiacum
Boletus rufus
Trachypus aurantiacus
Orange or Orange-Cap Boletus
Good

110 **BOLETUS SCABER**
(Bull. ex Fr.)
LECCINUM SCABRUM
(Bull. ex Fr.) S. F. Gray
Boletus Carpini (Schulz)
Trachypus Carpini
Rough-Stemmed Boletus
Good

111 **BOLETUS EDULIS** (Fries)
Bull. ex Fr.
Cep; Edible Boletus
Excellent

112 **BOLETUS FELLEUS** (Bulliard)
TYLOPILUS FELLEUS
(Bull. ex Fr.) Karst.
Gyroporus felleus
Bitter Boletus
Inedible

113 **BOLETUS CASTANEUS** (Bulliard)
GYROPORUS CASTANEUS
(Bull. ex Fr.) Quél.
Chestnut Boletus
Good

114 **BOLETUS AEREUS** (Fries)
Bull. ex Fr.
Excellent

115 **BOLETUS SATANAS** (Lenz)
Lenz
Satan's Boletus
Poisonous

116 **BOLETUS ALBIDUS** (Roques)
Inedible

117 **BOLETUS CYANESCENS** (Fries)
GYROPORUS CYANESCENS
(Bull. ex Fr.) Quél.
Indigo Boletus
Excellent

118 **BOLETUS PINICOLA** (Vittadini)
BOLETUS EDULIS subsp PINICOLA
(Vitt.) Konr. et Maubl.
Excellent

119 **BOLETUS CALOPUS** (Fries)
Pachypus calopus
Scarlet-Stemmed Boletus
Inedible

120 **BOLETUS LURIDUS** (Fries)
Schaef. ex Fr.
Lurid Boletus
Good with caution

121 **BOLETUS PULVERULENTUS**
(Opatowsky)
Xerocomus pulverulentus
Good

122 **BOLETUS BOVINUS** (Fries)
SUILLUS BOVINUS
Shallow-Pored Boletus; Cow Boletus
Edible

123 **BOLETUS CAVIPES** (Opatowsky)
BOLETINUS CAVIPES
(Opat.) Kalchbr.
Hollow-Stemmed Bolitinus
Edible

124 **BOLETUS VARIEGATUS** (Fries)
SUILLUS VARIEGATUS
Variegated Boletus
Edible

125 **BOLETUS SUBTOMENTOSUS** (Fries)
XEROCOMUS SUBMENTOSUS
(L. ex Fr.) Quél
Yellow-Cracked Boletus
Good

126 **BOLETUS BADIUS** (Fries)
XEROCOMUS BADIUS
(Fr.) Gilbert
Bay Boletus
Excellent

127 **BOLETUS GRANULATUS** (Fries)
SUILLUS GRANULATUS
(L. ex Fr.) O. Kuntze

Ixocomus granulatus
Granulated Boletus
Good

128 **BOLETUS LUTEUS** (Fries)
SUILLUS LUTEUS
(L. ex Fr.) S. F. Gray
Yellow-Brown Boletus
Good

129 **BOLETUS ELEGANS** (Fries)
SUILLUS ELEGANS
(Schumacher ex Fr.) Snell
Boletus flavus; Ixocomus flavus
Elegant Boletus
Good

130 **BOLETUS VISCIDUS** (Fries)
Viscid Boletus
Edible

131 **BOLETUS PARASITICUS** (Builliard)
XEROCOMUS PARASITICUS
Parasitic Boletus
Not recommended

132 **POLYPORUS OVINUS** (Fries)
SCUTIGER OVINUS
(Schaeff. ex Fr.) Murrill
Sheep Polyporus
Good

133 **POLYPORUS CONFLUENS** (Fries)
SCUTIGER CONFLUENS
(A. & S. ex Fr.) Bondarzew & Singer
Edible with caution

134 **POLYPORUS SQUAMOSUS** (Fries)
Melanopsis squamosus
Huds. ex Fr.
Dryad's Saddle
Edible with caution

135 **POLYPORUS SULPHUREUS** (Fries)
LAETIPORUS SULPHUREUS
(Bull. ex Fr.) Bondarzew & Singer
Tyromyces sulphureus
Chicken Mushroom
Edible when young

136 **POLYPORUS BETULINUS** (Fries)
PIPTOPORUS BETULINUS
(Bull. ex Fr.) Karst.
Birch Polyporus
Inedible

137 **POLYPORUS FRONDOSUS** (Fries)
POLYPILUS FRONDOSUS
(Dickson ex Fr.) Karst.
Fomes betulinus; Ungulina betulina
Hen-of-the-Woods
Good

138 **POLYPORUS UMBELLATUS** (Fries)
POLYPILUS UMBELLATUS
(Pers. ex Fr.) Bondarzew & Singer
Grifola umbellata
Umbellate polyporus
Good

139 **POLYPORUS LEUCOMELAS** (Fries)
Edible

140 **POLYPORUS PES-CAPRAE** (Persoon)
SCUTIGER PES-CAPRAE
(Pers. ex Fr.) Bondarzew
Good

141 **GANODERMA LUCIDUM** (Karsten)
(Leysser ex Fr.) Karst.
Polyporus lucidus
Lacquer Fungus; Shining Polyporus
Inedible

142 **FISTULINA HEPATICA** (Karsten)
Beefsteak Mushroom
Good

143 **PSEUDOHYDNUM GELATINOSUM**
(Fr.) Karst.
[Tremellodon] gelatinosum (Persoon)
White Jelly Mushroom
Edible

144 **HYDNUM REPANDUM** (Fries)
DENTINUM REPANDUM
(Fr.) S. F. Gray
Spreading Hydnum
Excellent

145 **HYDNUM IMBRICATUM** (Linnaeus)
(Fr.)
Sarcodon imbricatum
Imbricated Hydnum
Edible when young

146 **CLAVARIA FORMOSA** (Fries)
RAMARIA FORMOSA
(Fr.) Quél.
Formosa Coral
Inedible

147 **CLAVARIA AUREA** (Schaeffer)
RAMARIA AUREA
(Fr.) Quél.
Golden Coral
Edible

148 **CLAVARIA FLAVA** (Fries)
RAMARIA FLAVA
(Fr.) Quél.
Yellow Coral
Inedible

149 **CLAVARIA PALLIDA** (Bresadola)
RAMARIA MAIREI
Donk
Poisonous

150 **CLAVARIA BOTRYTIS** (Persoon)
RAMARIA BOTRYTIS
(Fr.) Ricken
Purple-Tipped Coral
Good

151 **CLAVARIA PISTILLARIS** (Linnaeus)
CLAVARIADELPHUS PISTILLARIS
(Fr.) Donk
Large-Clubbed Clavaria
Edible

152 **NEUROPHYLLUM CLAVATUM**
(Patouillard)
GOMPHUS CLAVATUS
Pers. ex S. F. Gray
Cantherellus clavatus
Clustered Chanterelle
Edible

153 **CANTHARELLUS CIBARIUS** (Fries)
(Fr.)
Chanterelle
Good

154 **CANTHARELLUS LUTESCENS** (Fries)
(Pers.) ex Fr.
Yellowish Chanterelle
Good

155 **CANTHARELLUS TUBAEFORMIS**
(Fries)
Cantharellus infundibuliformis
Tubaform Chanterelle
Edible

156 **CRATERELLUS CORNUCOPIOIDES**
(Persoon)
(L. ex Fr.) Pers.
Horn of Plenty
Good

157 **SPARASSIS CRISPA** (Fr.)
Massecola crispa
Cauliflower Mushroom
Good

158 **DICTYOPHORA DUPLICATA**
(Bosc & Fischer)
(Bosc) E. Fischer
Stinkhorn
Inedible

159 **CLATHRUS CANCELLATUS** (Linnaeus)
Clathrus ruber
Latticed Stinkhorn
Inedible

160 **LYCOPERDON MAXIMUM** (Schaeffer)
CALVATIA GIGANTEA
(Pers.) Lloyd
Lycoperdum giganteum;
Calvatia maxima
Giant Puffball
Excellent

161 **LYCOPERDON BOVISTA** (Linnaeus)
CALVATIA UTERIFORMIS
(Bull. ex Pers.) M. Moser
Lycoperdon caelatum
Collapsing Puffball; Mosaic Puffball
Excellent

162 **LYCOPERDON PERLATUM**
(Pers.)
Lycoperdon gemmatum (Batsch)
Gem-Studded Puffball
Good

163 **LYCOPERDON SACCATUM** (Wahl)
CALVATIA SACCATA

Elongated Puffball
Edible

164 **LYCOPERDON ECHINATUM** (Persoon)
Inedible

165 **LYCOPERDON PYRIFORME** (Schaeffer)
Pers.
Pear-Shaped Puffball
Edible

166 **BOVISTA NIGRESCENS** (Persoon)
Round Puffball
Edible

167 **GEASTRUM FIMBRIATUM**
(Persoon)
[Geaster] fimbriatus (Fries)
Fringed Geaster
Inedible

168 **SCLERODERMA AURATIUM** (Linneaus)
L. ex Pers.
Schleroderma vulgare
Common Scleroderma
Inedible

169 **GYROCEPHALUS RUFUS** (Brefeld)
PHLOGIOTUS HELVELLOIDES
(Fr.) Martin
Guepinia helvelloides
Apricot Jelly Mushroom
Good

170 **MORCHELLA ESCULENTA**
Pers. ex St. Amans
Morchella rotunda (Boudier)
Morel; Sponge Mushroom
Excellent

171 **MORCHELLA VULGARIS** (Persoon)
(Pers.) Boud.
Morel
Excellent

172 **MORCHELLA DELICIOSA** (Fries)
Morel; Delicious Morel
Excellent

173 **MORCHELLA CONICA** (Persoon)
Pers. ex Fr.
Morel; Conic Morel
Excellent

174 **MITROPHORA HYBRIDA** (Boudier)
MORCHELLA SEMILIBRA
(DC. ex Fr.) Lev.
Half-Free Morel
Good

175 **GYROMITRA ESCULENTA** (Fries)
(Pers.) Fr.
False Morel; Brain Mushroom
Good with great caution

176 **HELVELLA CRISPA** (Fries)
Fr.
Common Helvella
Good

177 **HELVELLA LACUNOSA** (Afzelius)
Afz. ex Fr.
Elfin Saddle
Edible

178 **HELVELLA INFULA** (Schaeffer)
GYROMITRA INFULA
(Schaeff. ex Fr.) Quél.
Hooded Helvella
Edible with caution

179 **PEZIZA ACETABULUM** (Linnaeus)
PAXINA ACETABULUM
(Linnaeus ex St. Amans) O. Kuntze
Acetabula vulgaris
Reticulated Peziza
Edible with caution

180 **PEZIZA VENOSA** (Persoon)
DISCIOTIS VENOSA (Pers.) Boudier
Veined Peziza
Good with caution

181 **PEZIZA AURANTIA** (Persoon)
ALEURIA AURANTIA

(Fr.) Fuckel
Orange Peel Peziza
Good

182 **PEZIZA ONOTICA** (Persoon)
OTIDEA ONOTICA
(Pers.) Fuckel
Orange-Ear Peziza
Edible

183 **PEZIZA EXIMIA** (Durieu & Leveille)
SARCOSPHAERA EXIMIA
(Durieu & Leveille) R. Maire
Edible with caution

184 **SPATHULARIA FLAVIDA** (Persoon)
Yellow Spathularia
Edible

185 **TUBER MAGNATUM** (Picco)
Piedmont's Truffle; White Truffle
Excellent

186 **TUBER MELANOSPORUM** (Vittadini)
Winter Truffle; Black Truffle
Excellent

MYCOLOGISTS

The abbreviations in the previous nomenclature refer to the following mycologists.

(A & S) **Albertini** & **Schweinitz**, Germans

(Bolt.) **J. Bolton**, English

(Bres.) **G. Bresadola**, Italian

(Bull.) **P. Bulliard**, French

(Curt.) **M. A. Curtis**, American

(DC) **A. P. de Candolle**, (Swiss)

(Fr.) **E. M. Fries**, Swedish

(Gill.) **C. C. Gillet**, French

(Huds.) **W. Hudson**, English

(Karst.) **P. A. Karsten**, Finnish

(Konr.) **P. Konrad**, Swiss

(L.) **Lineaus**, Swedish

(Maubl.) **A. Maublanc**, French

(Müll.) **O. F. Müller**, Danish

(Opat.) **W. Opatowsky**, German

(Pers.) **Chr. Persoon**, Dutch

(Quél.) **L. Quélet**, French

(Sacc.) **P. A. Saccardo**, Italian

(Schaeff.) **J. Chr. Schaeffer**, German

(Schw.) **L. Schweinitz**, German

(Scop.) **J. A. Scopoli**, Italian

(Secr.) **L. Secretan**, Swiss

(Sow.) **J. Sowerby**, English

(Vitt.) **C. Vittadini**, Italian

BIBLIOGRAPHY

Amann G., *Pilze des Waldes*, Melsungen 1962
Atkinson George F., *Mushrooms edible, poisonous etc.*, New York 1961

Becker G., *La vie privée des champignons*, Paris 1952
Beeli M. et De Keyser M. L., *Les champignos de Belgique, Bruxelles* 1922
Bötticher W., *Pilzverwertung und Pilzkonservierung*, München 1950
Bresadola G., *Funghi mangerecci e velenosi*, Trento 1932
Bresadola G., *Funghi mangerecci e funghi velenosi*, Trento 1954
Bresadola G., *Iconographia mycologica*, Milano 1927

Cavara F., *Funghi e tartufi*, Milano 1943
Costantin M. J. et Dufour M. L., *Nouvelle flore des champignons*, Paris 1947
Cool C. and van der Lek H. A. A., *Paddestoelenboek*, Amsterdam 1936
Christensen Clyde M., *Common edible mushrooms*, Minneapolis 1943
Corner E. J. H., *Clavaria and Allied Genera*, London 1950

Dennis R. W. G., *British cup fungi and their allies*, London 1960
Dennis R. G. W., *British Ascomycetes*, Verlag 1968
Dumée Paul, *Nouvel atlas de poche des champignons comestibles et vénéneux*, Paris 1905

Eifert Virginia S., *Exporing for mushrooms*, Springfield 1952

Ferri G., *Funghi mangerecci e velenosi*, Milano 1915

Gagliardi G. e Persiani G., *Funghi freschi e secchi - Tartufi*, Milano 1962
Gäumann E., *Morphologie und Entwicklungsgeschichte der Pilze*, Jena 1926
Gäumann E., *Die Pilze*, Basel 1949
Gramberg E., *Pilze der Heimat*, Leipzig 1939
Gray William D., *The Relation of Fungi to Human Affairs*, New York, 1959
Gussow H. T. and Odell W. S., *Mushrooms and toadstools*, Ottawa 1927

Haas H., *Pilze Mitteleuropas*, Stuttgart 1951
Habersaat E., *Schweizer Pilzflora*, Berne (div. éditions)
Habersaat E. et Kraft M. M., *Nos champignons*, Lausanne 1963
Hardy George A., *Some mushrooms and other fungi*, Victoria 1947
Heim Roger, *Fungi iberici*, Barcellona 1934
Heim Roger, *Les champignons*, Paris 1948
Heim Roger, *Les champignons d'Europe*, Paris 1957
Herter G., *Champignons comestibles*, Paris 1951
Hesler L. R., *Mushrooms of the great smokies*, Knoxville 1960

Iacevskii A. A., *Osnoy mikologhii*, 1933
Ingold C. T., *Dispersal in fungi*, London 1953
Ito Seiji, *Nippon kinrui-shi*, Tokio 1955

Jahn H. *Pilze rundum*, Hamburg 1949
Jaccottet J. et Robert P., *Les champignons dans la nature*, Neuchâtel 1925

Kavina, *Atlas of fungi*, London 1947
Kawamura Sei-ichi, *Genshoku Nihon kinrui zukan*, Tokio 1954
Kleijn J., *Forma e colore dei funghi*, Torino 1961
Kleijn J., *Mushrooms and other fungi*, Amsterdam 1961
Kleijn H., *Mushrooms and other Fungi*, Garden City, N. Y. 1962
Krieger L. C. C., *The mushrooms handbook*, New York 1936

Lange J., *Flora agaricina danica*, Kopenhagen 1935
Lange Morten, *Illustreret svampeflora*, Kopenhagen 1961

Lange Morten, *Svampe livet*, Kopenhagen 1961
Lange Morten & Hora F. Bayard, *A Guide to Mushrooms & Toadstools*, London, 1956
Lange J. E. und Lange M., *600 Pilze in Farben*, München 1964
Large E. C., *The advance of fungi*, London 1940
Lebedeva L., *Griby, zagotovka i pererahotka*, L. M. 1937
Lebedeva L. A., *Opredelitel shlapoc.nykn gribov*, 1949
Le Cerf R., *Cent champignons*, Paris
Le Gal M., *Promenades mycologiques*, Paris 1957
Loewenfeld Claire, *Britain's Wild Larder, Fungi*, London, 1956
Loireau M. L., *Le champignon de couche*, Paris 1950

McIlvaine Charles, *One Thousand American Fungi*, Indianapolis 1900
Mc Kenny Margaret, *Mushrooms of field and wood*, New York 1929
Mc Kenny Margaret, *The savory wild mushroom*, Washington 1962
Melzer V., *Atlas Holubinek*, Praha 1945
Michael-Hennig, *Handbuch für Pilzfreunde*, Jena 1958
Michael-Schulz-Hennig-Schäffer, *Für Pilzfreunde*, Leipzig 1927
Morandi L. e Balducci E., *I funghi*, Milano 1954

Neuhoff W., *Pilze Deutschlands*, Hamburg 1946
Nippon kingaku gakkai kajho, Tokio 1956

Penzig O., *Flora popolare italiana*, Genova 1924
Peyrot A. e Cortin B., *Funghi*, Torino 1962
Peter J., *Kleine Pilzkunde Mitteleuropas*, Zürich 1960
Pilát Albert, *Mushrooms*, Amsterdam 1954
Pilat & Usak, *A Handbook of Mushrooms*, London.
Pilat A., and Usak O., *Mushrooms and Other Fungi*, London, 1961
Pilát A. e Usák O., *Náse Houby*, Praga 1953
Pilát A., *Pilz-Taschenatlas*, Praga 1959
Pilze, Verlag für biohygiene, München 1964
Planches suisses de champignons, Union des sociétes suisse de mycologie, Zürich 1947
Polevitzkii N., *Gribnoi stol*, L. 1932
Porche F., *Guide de l'amateur de champignons*, Paris 1937
Portevin G., *Ce qu'il faut savoir sur le champignons bons et mauvais*, Paris 1935
Postma W. P. and Kleijn H., *Paddestoelen*, Haarlem 1952

Ramsbottom John, *Mushrooms and toadstools*, London 1953
Rauh Werner, *Unsere Pilze*, Heidelberg 1959
Ricken A., *Vademecum für Pilzfreunde*, Leipzig 1920
Ramain P., *Mycogastronomie*, Paris 1954
Ramsbottom J., *Poisonous fungi*, London and New York 1945
Rokuya Imazeki and Tsuguo Hongo, *Coloured illustrations of fungi of Japan*, Osaka 1957 (in Jappanese)
Rolfe R. F. and Rolfe F. W., *The romance of the fungus world*, London 1925
Romagnesi Henri, *Nouvel atlas des champignons*, Paris 1956
Romagnesi Henri, *Petit atlas des champignons*, Paris 1962

Schweizer Pilztafeln, Verband schweizerischer Vereine für Pilzkund, Zürich 1953
Singer Rolf, *The Agaricoles in Modern Taxonomy*, Weinheim, 1962
Smith Alexander H., *Mushrooms in their natural habitats*, Portland 1959
Smith Alexander H., *The mushrooms hunter's field guide*, Ann Arbor 1958
Stricker P., *Das Pilzbuch*, Karisruhe 1949
Swanenburg de Veye G. D., *Paddestoelen*, Naarden 1950

Thomas Wm. S., *Field book of common mushrooms*, New York 1948

Vasiliev A, i Kononov A., *Griby i ikh izpolsovanie*, M. L. 1932
Vasilkov B. P., *Geograficekogo rasprostranieniia shlapoc.nykh gribov*, M. L. 1955
Vasilkov B. P., *Jzucenie shlapoc.nykh gribov v SSSR*, M. L. 1953
Vasilkov B., *Siedobnyie e iadovityie griby srednei polosy evropeiskoi ciasti SSSR*, M. L. 1948
Viola S., *I funghi come sono*, Milano 1963
Vries G. A. (de), *Paddestoelen*, Zutphen 1955

Wakefield E. M. and Dennis W. G., *Common british fungi*, London 1950
Wakefield E. M., *Common fungi*, London 1954

Zangheri P., *Funghi mangerecci*, Novi Ligure 1960
Zee-Kruseman M. (van der) and Wittop Koning M., *Paddestoelen zoeken en eten*, Rotterdam 1948
Zeitlmayer Linus, *Knaurs Pilzbuch*, München 1955

GUIDE TO 186 MUSHROOMS

N. B. The American Edition of this guide has been updated. Please see the section on Nomenclature.

1 AMANITA CAESAREA

EXCELLENT   Cooked or raw.

HABITAT   Summer and autumn. Found in regions at the foot of mountains. In hardwood forests, especially oak, chestnut, and walnut; found rarely in coniferous forests. On sandy ground. In open, dry, and warm places.

N. B.   In the first stage of its development, this mushroom is completely enveloped in a white membrane known as the volva, or universal veil, which gives it the appearance of a small egg. When the volva opens, the red cap of the fungus resembles an egg yolk, and the stalk is yellow.

CAP   At first it is ovoid, then convex, and finally plane, though it is sometimes slightly concave. From 3-8 inches in diameter. The margin is striate at first and later becomes ridged, parallel to the gills below. The surface is usually a lovely orange, red-orange, or yellow-orange. Occasionally, however, it appears faded to a pale yellow-orange color. On rare occasions remains of the volva survive in the form of large white warts. The cuticle is smooth, a bit viscid, shiny, and easily detached.

GILLS   Close and interspersed with smaller gills. They are broad with a slightly floccose edge and are completely free from the stalk. Usually yellow, darker or lighter depending on the color of the cap.

STALK   Cylindrical and very thick. The base is slightly or distinctly bulbous and is enveloped by the volva. Brighter or draker yellow depending on the color of the cap. First it is full and then depressed.

RING   Broad and skirt-shaped. Yellow, brighter or darker depending on the color of the cap. The outer surface is grooved with vertical striation.

VOLVA   The margin has irregular lobes. It is largely detached from the base of the stalk it envelopes. White.

FLESH   White, but yellowish under the cuticle of the cap. The odor and taste are mild and pleasant.

MISTAKEN   For the **Amanita muscaria** 2, poisonous, which, however, almost always has remains of the volva on the cap in the form of warts. The volva adheres to the base in squamous belts; it has a brighter and more intense coloration. The gills, stalk, and ring are white, and only very rarely are they yellowish.

Amanita caesarea (Caesar's Agaric)

2 AMANITA MUSCARIA

POISONOUS   Very dangerous and occasionally even deadly. Nevertheless, in Europe it is eaten in some regions after the red cuticle of the cap has been removed or after boiling until the yellow scum it produces disappears; in some regions it is sold on the market. Siberian indians are reported to use this mushroom as an hallucinogen.

HABITAT   June until frost, but chiefly in the autumn. It is found in hardwood and conifer forests, particularly under birch and fir trees, and in open places and bushy pastures.

CAP   Ovoid at first, them hemispherical, and finally plane, and sometimes a bit depressed. From 3-8 inches in diameter. In mature examples, the margin is striate parallel to the gills below. The surface is usually a beautiful blood-red or red-orange although it may at times be yellow. The cap is almost always covered with white warts, remains of the volva; the more numerous the warts, the smaller they are. They may turn yellowish in the sun or be gradually worn away or washed off by rain. The cuticle is slightly sticky when the air is damp, and shiny when the air is dry.

GILLS   Close and occasionally interspersed with smaller gills. They are broad but become narrower near the stalk, from which they are free. White, occasionally with yellowish tinges.

STALK   Cylindrical. The base is bulbous and ovoid and is enveloped by an adhering volva. White with occasional yellowish tinges. At first it is covered with flocculi, and later it becomes glabrous. Smooth and occasionally striate in the zone above the ring. Full of pith but soon hollow. When the mushroom is picked and set down horizontally, it soon curves inward like wax. This phenomenon is also common to other species.

RING   Full and skirt-shaped. Cottony at first, and then membranous. Smooth and sometimes slightly striate. White, rarely yellowish. It has a cordlike edge of velvety yellow.

VOLVA   Attached to the bulbous base and formed of several belts of coarse scales. Hence it is inseparable from the base itself. White.

FLESH   Very firm but fragile. White. The flesh immediately under the cuticle of the cap is the same color as the cap but somewhat paler. The odor and taste are insignificant.

MISTAKEN   For the **Amanita caesarea** 1, an excellent mushroom, which, however, only rarely has warts on the cap. The stalk, ring, and gills are yellow. The volva surrounds the base but does not adhere to it.

Amanita muscaria (Fly Agaric)

3 AMANITA PANTHERINA (False Blusher; Panther Amanita; Panther Cap)

POISONOUS Like the **Amanita muscaria** 2, it is dangerous but rarely deadly.

HABITAT Late summer and autumn. In hardwood and conifer forests. The most dangerous mushroom in the Pacific Northwest.

CAP Hemispherical, then convex, and finally plane; sometimes slightly depressed. From 2-6 inches in diameter. Olive-brownish, brown-ochre, or grayish brown in color. The color is often darker at the center of the cap. Occasionally the cap is a faded whitish color. It is covered with small, floccose, and sharp-edged white warts, often arranged in very regular patterns. There is striation along the margin that turns into ridges in correspondence to the gills below. The cuticle is viscid when the air is damp; otherwise it is dry and shiny.

GILLS Close and interspersed with smaller gills. Broad and free from the stalk. White.

STALK Cylindrical. The base is in the form of a globular bulb with a distinct margin. White or whitish in color. It is delicately striate above the ring. Stuffed but soon hollow.

RING Full and skirt-shaped coming halfway down the stalk; it is often oblique. White and delicately striated. Soft and fragile. The ring wears away when the mushroom is fully matured, so that it does not appear at all in full-grown specimens.

VOLVA Attached to the bulb of the base, which it sheathes. It has a clearly defined margin. Two or three residual rings of the volva encircle the stalk just above the bulb of the base. Permanent.

FLESH Damp and white. The young fungus has a faint odor and flavor; the full-grown specimen has a disgusting odor and taste.

MISTAKEN For the **Amanita rubescens** (Blusher) 4, an excellent mushroom, whose flesh, however, turns slightly wine-red in color when it is cut and exposed to the air. That of the **Amanita pantherina** remains white. Sometimes mistaken for **Amanita porphyria**, a suspect fungus which has very few warts. These warts are formed by large pieces of the volva, often similar to pieces of lace ribbon, and the cap is grayish violet or grayish brown.

Amanita pantherina (False Blusher)

SUSPECT When raw.

EXCELLENT When properly cooked.

HABITAT Summer and autumn. In woods, particularly of conifers.

CAP Hemispherical at first, and then expanded. From 2 ½-5 ½ inches in diameter. Pale wine-red, brownish red, or purplish in color. Sometimes it is pale whitish. The center of the cap is usually darker in color. Covered with dry farinose warts, white, grayish, or yellowish in color.

GILLS Close and interspersed with smaller gills. Broad. Attached to the stalk only by a tooth. White and soft, they have reddish spots.

STALK Cylindrical and slightly cone-shaped. The base is bulbous. The zone above the ring is white and striate. Below the ring it is paler than the cap and a bit scaly. Full at first, then swollen, and finally hollow.

RING Skirt-shaped and full. White or pink, but sometimes chrome yellow. Striate.

VOLVA Usually only slight traces of the volva remain stuck to the bulb of the base.

FLESH Tender and white. When cut it turns slightly pale wine-red in color, especially the flesh of the base. Odorless. At first the flavor is pleasant, but it later becomes slightly bitter.

MISTAKEN For **Amanita pantherina** (False Blusher) 3, a poisonous fungus whose flesh does not turn wine-red in color but remains white. Mistaken for **Amanita porphyria**, a suspect fungus, which has cream-colored gills, a grayish-violet or grayish-brown cap, and is free of warts or has only a few large ones that often resemble pieces of lace or ribbon.

N. B. It is advisable for a person identifying a mushroom as **A. rubescens** for the first time to have his identification double-checked by a local mycologist before eating - it is not advisable to ever take chances with any **Amanitae**.

Excellent when cooked

Amanita rubescens (Blusher)

5 AMANITA CITRINA

INEDIBLE It is not poisonous, but since it is often difficult to distinguish it from the deadly **Amanita phalloides** 7, it is not advisable to gather. Furthermore the odor of the mature mushroom and the flavor of the cooked mushroom are not very pleasant.

HABITAT End of spring until autumn. In hardwood and conifer forests. On sandy dry ground.

CAP Ovoid at first, then convex, and finally expanded; sometimes slightly depressed in the center. From 2-4 inches in diameter. The margin is smooth and regular without striation. Its typical color is bright lemon yellow or bright chrome yellow, or bright greenish yellow. But there is a variety that is all white. It is covered wih large irregular cottony warts that are white at first and then brownish in color.

GILLS Close, unequal, and broad. The edge of the gills is delicately fringed. The whitish gills do not reach to the stalk.

STALK Cylindrical with a bulb-shaped base, globular and slightly squashed in appearance, with a clearly defined and stepped margin. White or slightly yellowish. Totally covered with furfuraceous particles that disappear as the fungus matures. It is striate above the ring. Full at first and then stuffed with a substance of slight consistency.

RING Skirt-shaped and large. The outer surface preserves the striation impressed by the gills to which it was attached. The inner surface is very cottony. The margin is fringed. The color is lemon yellow.

VOLVA Attached to the base and cracked. White with yellow ochre and brown patches.

FLESH White and tender. Under the cuticle of the cap it is pale lemon yellow. The young fungus has the odor of potato, while the mature fungus has an unpleasant odor. The flavor is pleasant at first, but it soon turns bitter.

MISTAKEN For **Amanita gemmata** 6, which is edible, but that fungus has a cap margin which is striate in correspondence to the gills below. Also mistaken for **Amanita phalloides** 7, which is deadly but does not have the odor of potato and has a base surrounded by a full volva, most of which is not attached to the base.

Amanita citrina (False Death Cap)

6 AMANITA GEMMATA

GOOD WITH CAUTION When it has been boiled and then kept some time in oil, it becomes excellent. However, on occasion it seems to have caused some slight disurbances, without serious consequences, in particularly sensitive people.

HABITAT From spring till autumn. In mountainous areas, rarely in the plains. In woodlands.

CAP Campanulate, almost conical at first, and later expanded. Sometimes it becomes concave. From 2-3 ½ inches in diameter. Slightly viscid. The margin is thin and generally striate in correspondence with the gills below. The cuticle sometimes has a few cottony white warts that remain from the volva, but it is often completely without warts. The cuticle is easily removed from the flesh of the cap. It is jonquil or narcissus yellow in color, often pale in tone, less frequently a deeper yellow. And sometimes it is reddish-yellow in color.

GILLS Close and broad with a fringed edge. They are very slightly attached to the stalk.

STALK Cylindrical and very delicate, it has an ovoid or globular bulb base. Whitish and fibrillose, it is full of a cottony substance at first and then hollow.

RING It is just above the middle of the stalk and white in color. It falls off and mature specimens often have no ring at all.

VOLVA Attached to the bulb. The margin of the volva often forms a kind of collar on the bulb.

FLESH Tender and fragile. White but yellowish under the cuticle of the cap. The odor and flavor are mild and pleasant.

MISTAKEN For **Amanita citrina** 5, which is inedible and has a smooth cap margin, in other words, without striation. Mistaken for **Amanita phalloides** 7, a deadly fungus that has a large volva around the base and is not attached to the base except underneath.

Good with caution

Amanita gemmata

7 AMANITA PHALLOIDES *

DEADLY   It remains deadly even when cooked or dried. See pages 32-33.

HABITAT   Summer and autumn in hilly and mountainous regions. Found also in hardwood forests, particularly under oaks, and also in conifer forests.

CAP   Globular at first, then hemispherical, and finally expanded and flattish. From 2-6 inches. A bit viscid when the air is damp; silky and shiny when the air is dry. The cuticle can be removed from the flesh of the cap. The typical color is green: olive, yellowish, or brownish; but it may be brown or almost white. Radiating from the center of the cap are darker striations, sharper or fainter depending on the general color. These striations do not reach all the way to the margin.

GILLS   Close, unequal, and broad. They are free from the stalk. They are white with greenish highlighting. When rubbed with the fingers, they do not change color. (Caution: wash hand well after picking any poison **Amanitae.**)

STALK   Cylindrical with a bulbous base enveloped by a large volva. White or whitish. Immature specimens sport white falling flocculi. Full or concave, stuffed or hollow.

RING   Full and skirt-shaped. White, or yellowish white. Striate. In exceptional cases the ring may disappear; some mature specimens appear without one.

VOLVA   Large and sack-shaped, irregularly lobed. The volva is sometimes regular in form without lobes. It is free of the base bulb for half of its length. White in color, but the interior of young specimens is often greenish yellow. **When picking mushrooms care should be taken that the volva is not left in the ground. The possession of a volva is a characteristic feature of the poisonous Amanitas.**

FLESH   White and slightly greenish under the cuticle of the cap, when the cap is greenish. Odorless. Older specimens have an odor of cadavers.

MISTAKEN   For **Amanita citrina** 5, which is inedible and has the volva attached to the base. Mistaken for **Amanita gemmata** 6, which is good and has the volva attached to the base. Mistaken for **Amanitopsis (Amanita) vaginata** 12, which is good but ringless. Mistaken for **Lepiota leucothites** 19, which is good but without the volva at the base. Mistaken for **Agaricus campestris** 24, and other **Agaricaes** but they lack a volva, have gills pinkish to tobacco brown in color, and turn reddish when rubbed. Mistaken for **Russula cyanoxantha** 88, **olivacea** 89, and **virescens** 90, all of which lack ring and volva. Mistaken for other **Amanitae** as well.

* The species that had been called **A. phalloides** in North-eastern United States for a long time is actually **A. brunnescens**, distinguished by a longitudinal split in the bulb of young specimens. For the collector, this description will serve for **A. brunnescens** as well.

Amanita phalloides (Death cap)

8 AMANITA VERNA

DEADLY   Poisonous even when cooked or dried. See pages 32-33.

HABITAT   From summer till autumn. Hence the name **Amanita verna**, or Spring Amanita, is not exact. It is found in hilly country and less frequently in mountainous country. In the woods. It is most common in limey soil.

CAP   Ovoid at first, then ever more flattened, and finally a bit depressed. From 2-4 inches in diameter. The margin is thin and not striate. The surface is smooth, but when the air is damp it becomes somewhat viscid. Otherwise it is dry, silky, and shiny. Occassionally there are some whitish warts, remains of the volva. It is white, occasionally ivory or pale ochre. It is somewhat darker in the center. When touched or rubbed, the color does not change.

GILLS   Close and vertical, interspersed with smaller gills that are cut off around the stalk. They are white and free from the stalk. The color does not change when the gills are touched or rubbed. (Caution: wash hands well after picking any poison **Amanitae**.)

STALK   Cylindrical and very slender. It is often very delicate. The bulbous base is enveloped by the volva. It is striate above the ring. Immature specimens have a stalk covered with furfuraceous flocculi. White and full, then stuffed with a cottony substance which later becomes cottony puffs, and finally totally hollow.

RING   Shirt-shaped in the upper third of the stalk's length. White and variously striate.

VOLVA   Slender and tight over the bulb of the base but generally detached from the rest. The margin is lobed. The white volva survives in the mature specimen. **When picking mushrooms care should be taken that the volva is not left in the ground. Serious accidents have been caused by such carelessness, for the possession of a volva is a characteristic feature of the poisonous Amanitas.**

FLESH   Tender and white. The immature fungus is almost odorless, while the full-grown fungus has an unpleasant odor.

MISTAKEN   For **Lepiota leucothites** 19, which is good but lacks the volva at the base. Mistaken for **Agaricus campestris** 24, which is good, and others of the same genus, all of which have gills the color of which varies from pinkish to tobacco brown. They are without volva at the base. When touched or rubbed they become spotted with color.

Amanita verna (Destroying Angel)

9 AMANITA VIROSA

DEADLY   Deadly even when cooked or dried. See pages 32-33.

HABITAT   From spring till autumn. In the woods. On sandy ground. Rare.

CAP   Globular at first, then conical, later campanulate, and finally expanded. It always has an umbo. From 1 1/2-4 inches in diameter. The margin is smooth, often with a ragged fringe, the remains of the partial veil, part of which forms the ring. The cuticle is viscid when the air is damp and can be removed from the flesh of the cap. White or ivory in color, it sometimes has shades of ochre in the center.

GILLS   Interspersed with many smaller gills and hence close, particularly towards the margin of the cap. They are not very long. They are white in color and do not touch the stalk.

STALK   Cylindrical and slender. The bulbous base is enveloped by the volva. The cuticle is ragged and rough and white in color. At first it is full of fibrous pith, and later it is hollow.

RING   Sometimes it remains attached here and there to the margin of the cap and appears torn. It is frequently oblique to the stalk. Thin, delicate, and white, it is covered with wooly flocculi.

VOLVA   The thick volva envelops the bulb of the base, but the upper portion is detached from the bulb. White. **When picking mushrooms care should be taken that the volva is not left in the ground. Serious accidents have been caused by such carelessness for the possession of a volva is a characteristic feature of the poisonous Amanitas.**

FLESH   Tender and white. The odor is rather unpleasant.

MISTAKEN   For **Lepiota leucothites** 19, a fine mushroom that has no volva at the base. Mistaken for **Agaricus campestris** 24, which is good, and for other fungi of the same genus, which are distinguished by the color of the gills, which ranges from pink to tobacco brown. They do not have a volva at the base. They generally bruise more or less noticeably when touched or rubbed.

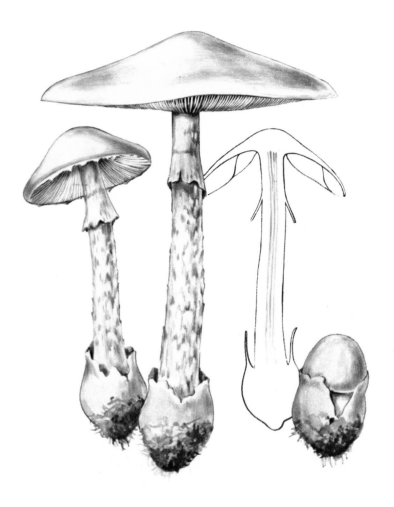

Amanita virosa (Destroying Angel)

10 AMANITA SOLITARIA (Woodland Amanita)

EDIBLE

HABITAT Summer and autumn. In less dense hardwood forests and parkland. On limey soil. Very rare.

CAP Almost spherical, then convex, and finally expanded, and sometimes slightly depressed. From 2½-8 inches in diameter. The margin is lightly striate. From the margin of the young fungus hangs a soft, white, and irregular piece of the partial veil, the remains of which go to form the ring. The surface is smooth and almost always covered with soft warts of various shapes, the remains of the general veil, the rest of which goes to form the volva. These warts soon take on a darker color than the cuticle of the cap. The color of the cap is pure white at first and light gray in the center; later it becomes totally grayish or yellowish gray.

GILLS Close, unequal, and broad. The edge is often slightly fringed. Detached from the stalk. White.

STALK Thick and cylindrical. White. The young fungus is covered with furfuraceous scaly matter that sticks to the fingers. The base is often bulbous and ovoid and almost always buried in the earth. The margin is not clean, and the surface is covered with scales. The volva is attached to the base and is not totally distinct.

RING Large, soft, farinose, and skirt-shaped. It is of the consistency of cream. White, delicate, and striate. It falls off easily, and mature specimens often lack a ring.

FLESH Tender and white. Almost odorless. Pleasant in taste.

MISTAKEN For **Amanita verna** 8, which is deadly, and **Amanita virosa,** 9, which is also deadly. But these fungi have membranous rather than creamy rings, while the volva surrounding the base is for the most part detached from the base, and they have warts on the cap only exceptionally.

Amanita solitaria (Woodland Amanita)

11 AMANITA OVOIDEA

GOOD

HABITAT Summer and autumn. In the woods. Chiefly on limey soil.

CAP Ovoid at first, then hemispherical, and finally expanded. From 4-12 inches in diameter. It is very fleshy. The margin turns slightly under and is smooth and covered with farinose flocculi. White.

GILLS Close and broad, they are interspersed with smaller gills. The edge of the gills is floccose. The gills, which are not attached to the stalk, are white at first and then turn a bit ivory in color.

STALK Cylindrical in form, it resembles a truncated cone. Large and solid, it is slightly bulbous at the base. White in color and covered with farinose flocculi.

RING White and thick but of the consistency of cream. It easily dissolves, and mature specimens often lack the ring.

VOLVA Large with a lobed margin. Sometimes white in color but more often yellowish or ochre. It survives in mature specimens.

FLESH Solid and white. Faint odor and flavor.

MISTAKEN For **Amanita verna** 8, deadly, and for **Amanita virosa** 9, deadly. But the general appearance of these fungi is quite different from that of **Amanita ovoidea** when examined attentively.

Good

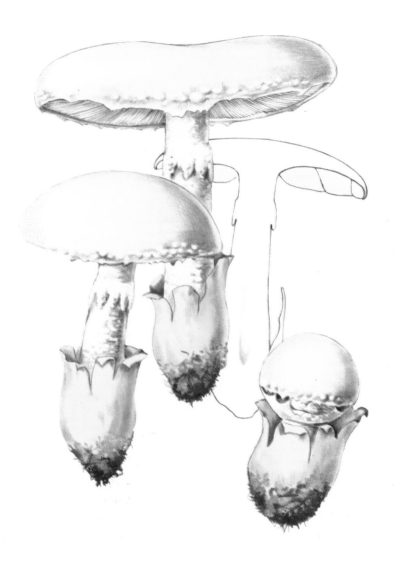

Amanita ovoidea

12 AMANITOPSIS VAGINATA AMANITA VAGINATA

GOOD   Especially the typical grayish form.

HABITAT   From May to October. In hardwood forests and less frequently in conifer woods. Chiefly on sandy ground. Very common.

CAP   Conical or campanulate at first and then expanded. It often has a slight umbo in the center. From 3/4-3 1/2 inches in diameter. The margin is striate in correspondence with the gills below. As the fungus develops the striations become grooves. Seen from above the cap resembles a buzz saw with triangular teeth. The surface is smooth and a bit viscid at the beginning. Color is extremely variable, from white to dark gray, olive, reddish brown, orange, or yellow. It is generally paler at the margin. The most typical form is grayish. It often has occasional broad and thick white warts. Occasionally there is only one wart but it may cover a large part of the cap.

GILLS   Close and equal. Free from the stalk. White.

STALK   Cylindrical, tending to conical. Slender, delicate, white or tinged with the same color as the cap. In the young specimen the stalk is covered with loose flocculi. Fragile. Full of pith at first, and later hollow. There is no ring.

VOLVA   Sac-shaped, high and narrow with a lobed margin. It envelops the base but is only attached at the bottom. White but occasionally tinged the same color as the cap, particularly on the inner side.

FLESH   Tender and fragile. White or the same color as the cap but much paler. Odor and flavor are almost unnoticeable.

MISTAKEN   For **Amanita pantherina** 3, poisonous, which can be distinguished, however, by the warts on the cap, the volva attached to the base, and a large ring. Mistaken for **Amanita porphyria**, suspect, which has cream-colored gills.

Amanitopsis (Amanita) vaginata (Grisette)

13 LEPIOTA PROCERA
MACROLEPIOTA PROCERA

(Parasol Mushroom)

EXCELLENT   Raw in salad or cooked on the grill or in a pan. Properly prepared, even naturally dried caps found on the ground can be eaten. The fibrous stalk should be discarded.

HABITAT   Summer and autumn. In less dense or trimmed woodlands. Particularly on gravelly ground.

CAP   Ovoid at first, then campanulate, later umbrella-shaped, and finally flat, always with an umbo in the center. From 4-10 inches in diameter. The cuticle of the umbo is smooth and brown, but as the fungus matures this cuticle is torn into warts that become less close-set away from the center of the cap and toward the margin. The cuticle below is grayish or nut brown and fibrillose; this cuticle also has scales. The margin is fringed.

GILLS   Close together, soft, white. Free from the stalk.

STALK   Cylindrical and generally slender. From 8-16 inches in height. Grayish, lighter toward the top. It is covered with delicate brownish scales in a zig zag pattern and looks something like a snakeskin. The bulbous foot is usually not cracked. The stalk is hard, fibrous, and hollow, and is easily detached from the cap.

RING   Full and formed of several thin fringed layers. White and scaly above and membranous below. It fits loosely around the stalk and when it is dry may slide down.

FLESH   Compact, tender, and white; sometimes it turns pinkish when cut. Pleasant odor; a soupy odor when the mushroom is drying. Pleasant flavor.

N. B.   The specimen illustrated on the facing page grew in a less sunny place and is smaller and darker than more typical specimens.

Lepiota (Macrolepiota) procera (Parasol Mushroom)

14 LEPIOTA RHACODES
MACROLEPIOTA RHACODES

(Shaggy Lepiota; Ragged Lepiota)

EXCELLENT Similar to **Lepiota (Macrolepiota) procera** 13. Discard the stalk.

HABITAT Summer and autumn. In woodlands, particularly coniferous, but also in cultivated fields. On humus-rich soil. Not very common.

CAP Globular at first, then convex, and finally expanded; there is sometimes a slight umbo in the center. From 2-6 inches in diameter. The cuticle is thick. The color is brown and gradually darkens as the fungus matures. At first it is solid, but it later breaks up into large stiff scales arranged in the fashion of roofing tiles. These are attached to the fibrils of the second cuticle, which is lighter in color and also breaks up into delicate scales. The margin is fringed.

GILLS Close and increasingly long toward the margin of the cap. They form an almost acute angle towards the stalk. Unequal in length. Very free from the stalk. White with a pinkish edge that later turns dark gray. They turn reddish at the touch.

STALK Cylindrical and slender, but at times it can be very short and squat. The bulbous spherical base is sometimes very large. White or grayish at first, and then brownish with reddish spots above the bulb. The center of the stalk is filled with pith the consistency of cobwebs.

RING Edged by a double row or fringe. The ring is movable on full-grown fungi and tends to slide down the stalk. Grayish white at first, turning reddish.

FLESH Tender and white, the flesh turns saffron yellow or reddish when it is broken or cut. Later it becomes brownish. Delicate and pleasant odor. Mild flavor and occasionally a bit unpleasant.

MISTAKEN For the poisonous **Lepiota (Leucocoprinus) molybdites** and the related **Lepiota (Leucocoprinus) Morgani**, distinguished by green gills in mature specimens. However, immature specimens cannot be differentiated from **L. rhacodes** except with the aid of a microscope. Button or half-mature specimens could be mistaken for the poisonous species and should be avoided.

Lepiota (Macrolepiota) rhacodes (Shaggy Lepiota)

15 LEPIOTA EXCORIATA

EXCELLENT Like **Lepiota (Macrolepiota) procera** 13.

HABITAT Summer and autumn. In conifer woods, along paths, in fields and cultivated land.

CAP Ovoid at first, then conical or campanulate, and finally almost flat, with a large umbo in the center. From 2-5 inches in diameter. The cuticle is light brown or walnut in color. Thin, finely granulose, and darker toward the center. It breaks up away from the margin of the cap and forms brownish fringes against a creamy white and silky underlayer. The margin peels and is light in color.

GILLS Close and thin and very broad. They are joined ring-fashion around the stalk, but they can be easily detached. Creamy white at first, brownish later.

STALK Cylindrical, tending to become conical in shape. The base is extremely bulbous. White and silky above the ring; whitish below the ring. Farinose or shaggy in texture and hollow.

RING Rigid and fringed. White with a brownish margin. Movable and tending to fall off. Consequently mature specimens often lack the ring.

FLESH Tender and white, it does not change color when cut. Pleasant odor. The flavor is somewhat acrid.

Lepiota excoriata (Flaky Agaric)

INEDIBLE It does not seem to be poisonous but the odor makes it inadvisable for eating.

HABITAT Summer and autumn in woodlands.

CAP Ovoid at first, then conical, and finally expanded with an umbo in the center. From 2-5 inches in diameter. The cuticle extends beyond the margin of the cap. It is brownish in color, generally paler along the margin, which is a creamy pinkish color. Fibrillose, it breaks up into large concentrically arranged pieces. Beneath these pieces is an off-white silky layer. The entire cuticle is covered with stiff conical scales. These scales fall off, so mature specimens often appear bare of them, partially or totally.

GILLS Very close and unequal. There is a furcate variety in which the gills are split. They are free from the stalk and not very broad. Creamy color tinged with pink.

STALK The height of the stalk is equal to the diameter of the cap in mature specimens. The strong stalk is bulbous at the base. Pale with pinks tinges in the upper part; below it is the color of the cap. Wooly and fibrillose. Towards the bulb of the base it is sometimes covered with scales similar to those on the cap. Full, then pithy, and later hollow but covered with a spongy white substance.

RING Large and skirt-shaped, edged with brownish scales similar to those on the cap. It survives in the fullgrown specimen.

FLESH Thick and fragile. The white flesh smells strong and disagreeably of oily rags. The taste is acid.

Lepiota acutesquamosa (Squarrose Agaric)

17 LEPIOTA CRISTATA (Stinking Agaric)

SUSPECT   Probably due only to its strong taste and odor.

HABITAT   Summer and autumn, in woodlands and fields.

CAP   Campanulate, then plane with a brown umbo in the center. From 3/4-2 inches in diameter. The scales around the umbo are of the same color as the umbo; they become smaller and less frequent away from the center of the cap. The cuticle is off-white and silky. The margin is curled under, almost forming a right angle to the surface of the cap. Sometimes it is irregularly undulate and lobed.

GILLS   Close, thin, and broad. Clearly free from the stalk. White.

STALK   Slender and delicate. Cylindrical and sometimes tapering toward the cap. The base is slightly bulbous. White, occasionally tinged with yellow. Silky and fragile. Hollow.

RING   Rather large. Turned upward with a clawlike edge or skirt-shaped. It tends to fall off, and full-grown specimens often lack the ring.

FLESH   White. Strong and fishy odor. Nauseating taste.

Lepiota cristata (Stinking Agaric)

18 LEPIOTA HELVEOLA

DEADLY It has resulted in fatal poisoning, similar to that caused by the deady **Amanitae**: **phalloides** 7, **verna** 8, and **virosa** 9.

HABITAT Summer and autumn. In airy woods, fields, and gardens. Among clover. Not common.

CAP Convex, then plane-convex, with a slight and sometimes insignificant umbo in the center. It is sometimes sunken in like a large and irregular goblet. From 3/4-2½ inches in diameter. The margin is thin, and in the mature fungus it is often undulate. Sometimes there are cracks in the same direction as the gills below. The cuticle is nut brown or brick in color. Dry and velvety, it quickly breaks up into concentric zones, more or less regularly arranged. The cuticle remains whole in the center, however. The color of these patches is pale ochre, but it changes to pinkish ochre when the fungus is picked.

GILLS Very close and unequal. Very broad. Clearly detached from the stalk. The edge is broken. White at first, then creamy in color.

STALK Cylindrical and rather slender. Not bulbous. Pale at first, then flesh pink, and finally light reddish brown. Dry and silky. It has a semi-developed brownish ring. The inside soon becomes pithy and silky, and later is hollow.

FLESH Thin and white, it turns pinkish when cut. Slight taste and odor, but the odor given off by several specimens kept in a closed receptacle is rather sweet.

Lepiota helveola

19 LEPIOTA LEUCOTHITES
(LEPIOTA NAUCINA)

(White Lepiota; Smooth Lepiota)

GOOD Take care with identification.

HABITAT Summer and autumn. In meadows, fields, copses, orchards, and gardens.

CAP Ovoid, then campanulate, and finally expanded. The center is flattened or raised in the form of a large umbo. Sometimes, however, it is a bit depressed. From 1½-5 inches in diameter. At first the surface is dewy moist to the touch, then smooth or slightly granulose. The cuticle is often cracked from dry wind. Completely white at first, it turns a dull palish white tinged with gray or light brown.

GILLS Close and thin, unequal. The edge is slightly undulate. Broad. Free but close to the stalk. Ivory in color at first, then flesh pink, and finally a purplish gray.

STALK Cylindrical, tending to conical in shape, with a swelling base. White, fibrillose, silky, and glabrous. Full at first, hollow later.

RING Small and fragile. The margin is ragged. It is on the upper part of the stalk. White and tending to fall off. Mature specimens often lack a ring.

FLESH Tender and white. It turns yellowish at the touch. The flesh of the bulb is reddish in mature specimens. The odor and taste are mild and pleasant.

MISTAKEN For **Amanita verna** 8, deadly, and **Amanita virosa** 9, deadly, both of which have a volva at the base and white gills that do not discolor when bruised. The gills of **L. leucothites** will turn brown on cooking.

Lepiota leucothites (White Lepiota)

GOOD   It was once considered poisonous, even deadly poisonous, because it was mistaken for the deadly **Amanitae**.

HABITAT   Summer and autumn, until the beginning of winter. In fields, meadows, and orchards. On garbage, dung, ruins, and around piles of straw left lying on the ground.

CAP   Campanulate at first, then expanded, often with a broad or slightly pronounced umbo in the center. From 1½-4½ inches in diameter. The margin is often irregular. Mature specimens are often marked by grooves or striations, short in length, above the gills. Viscid when the weather is damp; bright, when the weather is dry. Smooth. Glabrous. Only occasionally are there a few warts surviving from the volva. White or white tinged an ashy gray.

GILLS   Close and interspersed with smaller gills. The edge is floccose. Broad. Not attached to the stalk and in some cases distant from it. White, then pink, and finally brownish pink.

STALK   Cylindrical or elongated truncated cone in form. Slender and sometimes curving in. White with grayish tinges. Smooth. Full or stuffed with pith, but not hollow.

VOLVA   Thin. The margin is generally lobed. Sometimes it is closely attached to the base and may pass unobserved. White.

FLESH   Tender and white. It has no particular odor or taste.

MISTAKEN   For **Amanita phalloides** 7, deadly, when this fungus is faded in color. Mistaken for **Amanita verna** 8, deadly, and for **Amanita virosa** 9, deadly. But these three deadly poisonous Amanitas always have white gills and a ring around the stalk that only in exceptional cases disappears.

N. B.   Growing alongside **Volvariella speciosa** var. **speciosa** one may find specimens of **Volvariella speciosa** var. **gloiocephala** 21, good.

Volvariella speciosa var. speciosa (Dunghill Agaric)

GOOD   It was once considered poisonous, even deadly poisonous, because it was mistaken for some of the deadly **Amanitae**.

HABITAT   Summer and autumn, until the beginning of winter. In fields, meadows, and orchards. On garbage, dung, ruins, and around piles of straw left lying on the ground.

CAP   Campanulate at first, then expanded, often with a broad or slightly pronounced umbo in the center. From 1 1/2-4 1/2 inches in diameter. The margin is often irregular. Mature specimens are often marked by grooves or striations, short in length, above the gills. Viscid when the weather is damp; bright, when the weather is dry. Smooth. Glabrous. Only occasionally are there a few warts surviving from the volva. Smoky gray, or brownish gray, nutty or smoky brown, occasionally with a tinge of olive.

GILLS   Close and interspersed with smaller gills. The edge is floccose. Broad. Not attached to the stalk and in some cases distant from it. White, then pink, and finally brownish pink.

STALK   Cylindrical or elongated truncated cone in form. Slender and sometimes curving inward. White with grayish tinges. Smooth. Full or stuffed with pith, but not hollow.

VOLVA   Thin. The margin is generally lobed. Sometimes it is closely attached to the base and may pass unobserved. White.

FLESH   Tender and white. It has no particular odor or taste.

MISTAKEN   For **Amanita phalloides** 7, deadly, when this fungus is faded in color. Mistaken for **Amanita verna** 8, deadly, and for **Amanita virosa** 9, deadly. But these three deadly poisonous **Amanitae** always have white gills and a ring around the stalk that only exceptional cases disappears.

N. B.   Growing alongside this Dunghill Agaric, **Volvariella speciosa** var. **gloiocephala**, one may find specimens of **Volvariella speciosa** var. **speciosa** 20, good.

Volvariella speciosa var. gloiocephala (Dunghill Agaric)

GOOD

HABITAT Summer and autumn. On old decomposing hardwood trunks.

CAP Hemispherical or ovoid, later campanulate, and finally expanded. From 3-5 inches in diameter. White or off-white in color, silky, covered with very fine scales or fibrils, nut-brown in color.

GILLS Close. Sometimes mature specimens have gills with toothed edges. They do not touch the stalk. White at first and then pink.

STALK Cylindrical or elongated truncated cone in form. Often curved. Strong, white, and full.

VOLVA Very large and enveloping almost half the stalk. The margin is lobate. White at first, then off-white with brownish patches here and there.

FLESH Tender and white. The odor is mild and the taste is pleasant.

Volvariella bombycina (Silky Agaric)

23 PLUTEUS CERVINUS

EDIBLE.

HABITAT Summer and autumn. In woodlands. On decomposing trunks and branches, and on decomposing wood and on timber detritus.

CAP Campanulate at first, then plane-convex, with a large umbo in the center. From 2½-5 inches in diameter. The margin is usually smooth. Very rarely is it striate in correspondence to the gills below. The cuticle is glabrous. It is viscid when the air is damp and is brown or dark brown in color. As the fungus ages, the cap becomes very fibrous, covered with scales, and cracks.

GILLS Close and interspersed with smaller gills. Broad. Not attached to the stalk, the gills are white at first and then turn pink.

STALK Cylindrical or truncated cone in form. The height varies. The stalk is often bent like a coat hook. It is rather thick at the base. White or off-white in color, it is covered with brown fibers. Full.

FLESH Tender and white, almost colorless. It is almost odorless and without taste, or smells very weakly of almonds.

Pluteus cervinus (Deer Mushroom)

EXCELLENT This fungus can be eaten raw or cooked as well as dried for later use. The "cultivated" mushroom sold in stores in the United States, **A. bisporus**, is so closely related to **A. campestris** that they were long thought to the identical.

HABITAT It appears in late summer in the U. S. and survives into autumn. In all fertilized ground: fields, meadows, gardens, cultivated fields, and along foot-paths. It grows in groups, often circular in form.

CAP Hemispherical at first, then convex, and finally expanded. It is sometimes slightly concave in form. From 2-6 inches in diameter. The margin stays curved under toward the gills for a long time. It curves back when the mushroom is fully mature. White or off-white in color, it often turns yellow when bruised. Sometimes it is smooth and silky to the touch; sometimes it is velvety; and sometimes it is covered with brownish fibrils or scales.

GILLS Close and interspersed with smaller gills. Broad. Rounded towards the stalk, from which they are free. As the fungus matures, the gills turn from pink to tobacco brown in color.

STALK Cylindrical and rather short. White or slightly pink in color, it sometimes has darker patches, particularly toward the bottom. Smooth, firm, and full. Later it is stuffed with pithy matter.

RING Simple, thin, white, and fragile. It tends to fall, and mature specimens lose it.

FLESH Solid and white, it turns pink when exposed to the air, particularly the flesh under the cuticle and that of the base. The odor is mild, and the taste is pleasant.

MISTAKEN For **Amanita phalloides** 7, deadly, when this fungus is pale in color. Mistaken for the deadly **Amanita verna** 8 and the deadly **Amanita virosa** 9. These deadly **Amanitae**, however, always have white gills in every phase of their development. They do not change color when bruised and have a volva at the base. The mushroom hunter should be careful not to leave the volva in the ground. Carelessness of this kind can result in serious danger, as identification might not be accurate without it.

N. B. There are many species of Meadow Mushroom. The larger species, such as **Agaricus augusta**, which can grow up to 8 inches in diameter, and **Agaricus villatica**, which grows up to 15 inches in diameter, are certainly edible. The specimen illustrated on the facing page, left, below, is of the variety **umbrina**.

Agaricus campestris (Meadow Mushroom)

EXCELLENT This fungus can be eaten raw or cooked. It can also be dried.

HABITAT Summer and autumn. In woodlands, particularly coniferous.

CAP Convex, then expanded, flat or even concave. Occasionally it has a slight umbo in the center. From 2-4 inches in diameter. Whitish in color but totally covered, particularly toward the center, by yellowish-brown or reddish-brown scales. These scales are often joined to form large triangular scales.

GILLS Close and intespersed with smaller gills. Broad. Thin and free from the stalk. Pink in color at first, then brownish, and finally tobacco brown. The edge is paler and floccose.

STALK Cylindrical or rather conical. Quite long. The bulbous base does not have a clearly defined margin. Off-white in color at first, brownish or grayish tinges appear later. The zone below the ring is slightly floccose. Full of pith, later hollow.

RING Full and rather high up the stalk. Above it is white and somewhat striate; underneath it is covered with flocculi. The ring turns brownish in color.

FLESH Tender and white, it turns pink when exposed to the air. Later it turns a tobacco brown color. It has a pleasant odor and a good taste.

MISTAKEN For the deadly **Amanita phalloides** 7, when this fungus does not have its typical green color. Mistaken for the deadly **Amanita verna** 8 and the deadly **Amanita virosa** 9. These deadly **Amanitae**, however, always have white gills in every phase of development, and they have a volva at the base. The mushroom hunter should pay particular attention not to leave the volva in the ground. Carelessness of this kind may result in serious accidents, as identification might not be accurate without it.

N. B. There are many other species of this genus of fungus. The larger species, such as **Agaricus augusta**, which grows up to 8 inches in diameter, and **Agaricus villatica**, which grows up to 15 inches in diameter, are edible.

Excellent

Agaricus silvaticus (Wood Agaric)

26 AGARICUS ARVENSIS (Horse Mushroom; Plowed-Land Mushroom)

EXCELLENT This fungus can be eaten raw or cooked. It can also be dried.

HABITAT Summer and autumn. In woodlands and fields.

CAP Campanulate or finger-shaped at first, then convex, and finally expanded. From 2-8 inches in diameter. Smooth and glabrous. Always dry to the touch. Shiny as if polished. White at first, but later some pale lemon yellow patches appear, and finally light brown in color. The margin is usually regular and is sometimes edged with remains of the partial veil, the rest of which forms the ring.

GILLS Close and interspersed with smaller gills. Very broad. The edges are rounded towards the margin of the cap and toward the stem, from which they are free. White at first, then pinkish gray, and finally tobacco brown to brownish red in color, with lighter edges.

STEM Cylindrical and slender. The base is broader, usually on one side only. The zone above the ring is slightly violet in color; the zone below the ring is white at first, then patched with pale lemon yellow, and finally nut brown in color. Full but soon hollow. The pith is inconsistent and silky white in appearance.

RING Full. It has the form of a double-skirt. The outer one is membranous, the inner one is floccose. The margin is ragged. White and occasionally brownish. The ring tends to fall off, and mature specimens often are without it.

FLESH Solid and white, tending to turn yellowish and then pink. The odor resembles anise. The taste is mild.

MISTAKEN For the deadly **Amanita phalloides** 7, when this fungus appears without its typical green color. Mistaken for the deadly **Amanita verna** 8 and the deadly **Amanita virosa** 9. These three deadly **Amanitae**, however, always have white gills in every phase of their growth, and they have a volva at the base. The mushroom hunter is advised not to leave the volva in the ground. Carelessness of this kind may result in serious accidents, for identification will not be accurate.

N. B. There are many other species of this genus of fungus. The larger species, such as **Agaricus augusta**, which grows up to 8 inches in diameter, and **Agaricus villatica**, which grows up to 15 inches in diameter, are edible. Variable reactions to **A. arvensis** variety **palustris** have been reported.

Agaricus arvensis (Horse Mushroom)

SUSPECT This fungus can cause stomach ache to susceptible people.

HABITAT Summer and autumn. In woodlands, parks, along hedges and the edge of fields. It often grows in fairy rings.

CAP Tight campanulate or less frequently globular at first, later expanded and sometimes depressed. From 2-4 inches in diameter. At first the margin is curled under toward the gills, but it later turns out normally. The surface is glabrous, silky, and shiny. The color is dirty white with an occasional brownish patch in the center. When bruised it instantly turns a lemon yellow color. Slowly these bruises turn brownish in color.

GILLS Close and interspersed with smaller gills. Not very broad. They grow narrower near the margin of the cap and toward the stalk. White at first, then bright pink, and finally tobacco brown. The edge is lighter and uneven.

STALK Cylindrical with a more or less bulbous base and a well-defined margin to the base. White with light brown patches. When bruised, particularly around the base, it immediately turns lemon yellow. Silky and smooth. Stuffed with pith at first and then hollow.

RING Full. Thin at the top, it thickens toward the margin. It is somewhat striate above; underneath it is sometimes floccose. White with a yellowish margin.

FLESH Tender and white. The flesh of the base is often lemon yellow in color. All the flesh turns slightly yellow when exposed to the air. As the flesh ages it turns brown with darker areas that are almost black. It has a strong inky odor.

Agaricus xanthodermus (Yellow-staining Mushroom)

GOOD When the fungus is young. As it turns blackish it is no longer edible. It should be eaten the day it is picked, for it does not keep well.

HABITAT Summer and autumn. In orchards, gardens, parks, and along footpaths, wherever the soil is well fertilized, and particularly on deposits of limey material. It grows in clusters.

CAP Elongated oval, almost cylindrical at first; later it becomes campanulate. From 2-3½ inches in diameter. White, but brownish and yellowish at the top; pink along the margin. As the fungus matures the cuticle gradually darkens in color, turning dark gray or nut brown. The scales disappear and a fibrous fringe appears in regularly arranged concentric circles. Then the margin breaks along the lines of the gills below, and it starts to curl outward. In the end the cap gradually disappears, from the margin inward, until all that remains is a globule the color of India ink.

GILLS At first they touch, like segments of an orange; later they withdraw a bit. They are thin and interspersed with smaller gills. The edge is farinose. Free from the stalk. White at first, they later turn pink, beginning at the edge. Then they turn black, but by that time they have been transformed into shapeless blobs dripping from the margin of the cap.

STALK Cylindrical and slender; the base is almost always a bit bulbous. White and covered with a fine hairy growth; later it turns off-white, glabrous, and becomes covered with silky fibrils. Hollow, it contains a string of silvery white silky substance. In mature specimens this stringy part is generally noticeable only toward the base and resembles a Chinese pigtail. Specimens taller than 20 inches have been found in the United States.

RING White and thin, detached from the stalk. It tends to slide down. Mature specimens often lack a ring.

FLESH Tender and watery. White with mild odor and taste.

Coprinus comatus (Shaggy Mane)

EDIBLE WITH CAUTION When immature. When it begins to turn black, it is no longer edible. It should be eaten the day it is picked, for it can be kept only a short time. Sometimes it can cause mild poisoning, albeit temporary and not serious, when it is eaten with wine or other alcoholic beverages. The symptoms are heart palpitations, flushed face, sweating, cold hands and feet.

HABITAT From spring till autumn. On buried roots and trunks. It sometimes appears to be a terrestrial fungus, but it is actually lignicolous. In gardens, along roads, in grassy and shady places. It grows in clusters.

CAP Ovoid at first, then campanulate, and finally with the margin curving outward and up. From 1-3 inches in diameter. Deep groves radiating from the center toward the margin, where they are even deeper. The margin is thin and undulate. As the fungus matures the margin of the cap breaks along the lines of the gills below. Then it decomposes into a violet-black blob. The cuticle is grayish and brownish white at first, and darker at the top of the cap. Later it turns dark brown and then dark gray-brown. The edges of the grooves and cracks later turn purple.

GILLS Very close and broad. They are free of the stalk. Pale at first, they later turn brown with purple tinges. Finally they turn black with green or purple tinges.

STALK Cylindrical or very slightly swelling out from the bottom to the top. Squat at first, but later slender. White at first, it turns off-white as the slender brownish fibrils form. Silky and shiny. It has a hard thick consistency and is completely hollow.

RING Whitish, it is located just above the base of the stalk. It is firmly attached to the stalk, but soon disappears.

FLESH Delicate, brownish gray but then turning off-white in color. Pleasant odor and mild taste.

Coprinus atramentarius (Inky Cap)

SUSPECT Some say it is poisonous; others say it is edible.

HABITAT From early summer well into autumn in the U. S. On or near tree stumps. Not only outdoors but in natural and artificial caves. Generally in clusters of 10 to 100.

CAP Globular at first, then hemispherical, and finally expanded. Generally cuspidate on top or with a large umbo in the center. Sometimes, however, there is a concave pit at the center of the cap. From 3/4-2 3/4 inches in diameter. At first the margin curls down and under, toward the gills. And it often carries a yellow fringe, the remains of the partial veil. The cuticle is lemon or chrome yellow, but darker, even a rusty color, toward the center. It is smooth and glabrous.

GILLS Very close and interspersed with many smaller gills. Not very broad. Attached to the stem. At first they are chrome yellow, but they later turn olive in color, and are finally dark olive brown.

STALK Cylindrical and slender, delicate and curving. The base is pressed by the bases of the other specimens in the cluster. Lemon yellow, chrome yellow, or yellowish in color. The base is darker, sometimes brownish. Fibrillose and covered with falling flocculose matter. On the upper part are remains of one or more pseudo-rings, but these tend to disappear as the fungus matures and often disappear completely. Hollow and empty.

VEIL In immature specimens the cortina extends from the cap margin to the stalk. Yellowish in color, it retreats to form a yellowish pseudo-ring on the stalk, but this usually disappears. Sometimes part of the veil remains attached to the cap margin in the form of a fringe.

FLESH Quite yellow, it tends to turn reddish. The odor is unpleasant, and the taste is very bitter.

MISTAKEN For the edible **Armillariella (Armillaria) mellea** 61, for the good **Collybia (Flammulina) velutipes** 46, and for the good **Pholiota (Kuehneromyces) mutabilis** 35, but its bitter taste distinguishes it from all of these. Also mistaken for the suspect **Hypholoma (Naematoloma) sublateritium** 31, which is brick red in color, has white flesh, and is only slight bitter or not bitter at all; and for the edible **Hypholoma (Naematoloma) capnoides**, which has pale gray gills and is only slightly bitter.

Hypholoma (Naematoloma) fasciculare (Sulphur Tuft)

HYPHOLOMA SUBLATERITIUM (Brick Cap; Red Sulphur Tuft)
NAEMATOLOMA SUBLATERITIUM

SUSPECT Some claim that it is posonous; others say that it is edible. One would do better not to try it.

HABITAT Summer. On old tree trunks. It grows in clusters.

CAP Globular, then hemispherical or flattened campanulate in form, and finally expanded. From 2-3½ inches in diameter. The margin curves in toward the gills at first, but later bends back. The margin of immature specimens sometimes has a fringe, the remains of the veil. Glabrous and dry. Brick red in the center and paler toward the margin.

GILLS Close and interspersed with smaller gills. Not very broad blades. Attached to the stalk, sometimes only uncinate. Yellowish white at first, then olivegray, and finally chocolate in color. The edge is paler.

STALK Cylindrical and slender. Curved. The upper part preserves traces of a dark brown or black pseudo-annulus. Yellowish in color, but brick red at the base. Hollow.

VEIL In the immature fungus the veil extends from the cap to the stalk. Made of silky fibrils. At first it is whitish, and later it becomes dark brown or black. As the fungus matures, the veil withdraws as a pseudo-ring around the stalk. Dark brown or black in color, it gradually disappears altogether. Sometimes part of it remains attached to the margin of the cap forming a sort of fringe.

FLESH Yellowish. Under the cuticle of the cap and towards the base it is slightly brick red in color. Odorless. The taste is not unpleasant or just slightly bitter.

MISTAKEN For the inedible **Hypholoma (Naematoloma) fasciculare** 30, which is very bitter in taste. Mistaken for **Pholiota (Kuehneromyces) mutablilis** 35, a good mushroom that has a mild and pleasant taste. Mistaken for **Hypholoma (Naematoloma) capnoides**, an edible mushroom that has an ochre-colored cap rather than a brick red one. Mistaken for **Armillariella (Armillaria) mellea** 61, a good mushroom, but one that has gills decurrent along the stalk.

Hypholoma (Naematoloma) sublateritium (Brick Cap)

32 PHOLIOTA AERGERITA
AGROCYBE AEGERITA

EXCELLENT This fungus has a delicate flavor. It can also be kept dried or marinated. It is prized in Europe where it it cultivated, especially in Italy.

HABITAT From spring till the beginning of winter and even during mild winter weather. It grows on old stumps of poplar, willow, elm, elder, figs, and other hardwood trees, whether the stumps are dead or live. **Pholiota (Agrocybe) aegerita** grows in clusters and can be cultivated in the garden.

CAP Hemispherical at first, then plane, and finally concave. From 1-4 inches in diameter. At first the margin curves under toward the gills, but later unbends. It remains thin and becomes undulate. Finally it cracks along the lines of the gills underneath. The cuticle is smooth, dry, and silky at first, but later becomes ridged. The edges of the ridges are darker than the rest of the cuticle. Later it splits, particularly along the margin. The color varies from off-white or tan to white, red, and brown. When the fruiting body first appears the cap is dark brown. It is always darker toward the center. Specimens that have matured in shady areas often have a white cap or a cap that is white along the margin.

GILLS Close and broad. Attached to the stalk, uncinate. The edge of the gill is pale and often toothed. Off-white at first, then grayish yellow or tobacco colored.

STALK Cylindrical and generally long. It is often bent. The stalk is narrower at the base and curves in toward the cap. White at first, then brownish. Silky and fibrillose, and covered with delicate fur. The portion just below the cap is covered with flocculose matter. Strong, fibrous, and full.

RING Broad at first but it gradually disappears as the fungus matures. Situated high on the stem. The white surface curves up and is slightly ochre in color.

FLESH Generally fragile. It is white at first but later it turns a brownish yellow, particularly the flesh of the base. The odor is strong and not easily defined. The taste is pleasant.

Pholiota (Agrocybe) aeregita

33 PHOLIOTA DESTRUENS

NOT RECOMMENDED

HABITAT Summer and autumn, on poplar, willow, and birch trunks.

CAP Convex at first, then often very plane; it almost always has an umbo in the center. From 2 1/2-8 inches in diameter. Slightly viscid. The color varies: pale gray, yellow, or light brown; it is often much darker at the center. Covered with scales or large segments, sometimes arranged like roofing tiles to the margin of the cap. The margin curves under toward the gills. Remains of the partial veil hang from the margin.

GILLS Rather close and interspersed with smaller gills. Broad. Attached to the stalk by a tooth or more extensively. Whitish at first, then light brown.

STALK Cylindrical or truncated cone in form. Thick and even thicker at the base. Frequently curved. It is somewhat lighter in color than the cap. From the ring down it is covered with cottony scales turned upward. Hard and full.

RING Floccose. Mature specimens often retain only a trace of the ring.

FLESH Solid and white, tending toward the nut brown color of the stalk. Sometimes there is no odor at all, and sometimes the odor is disagreeable. Taste may be cloyingly sweet or bitter.

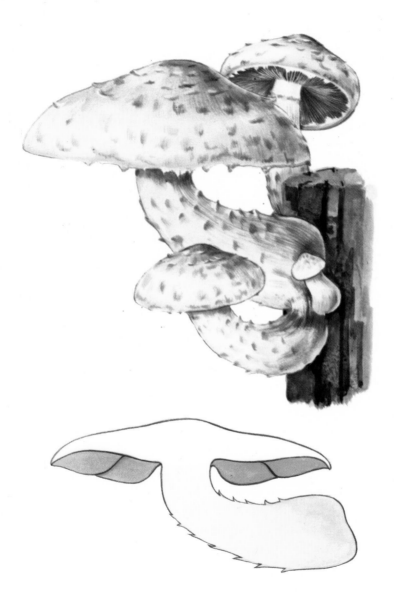

Pholiota destruens

PHOLIOTA SQUARROSA (Scaly Pholiota; Scaly Cluster Fungus)

EDIBLE But indigestible. Before cooking it in sauce, it should be boiled for several minutes. The water used to boil the fungus should be thrown away.

HABITAT Toward the end of summer and into autumn. In the vicinity of hardwood and conifer stumps, dead or live. It grows in clusters.

CAP Hemispherical at first, then convex, and finally expanded. From 2-5 inches in diameter. The margin curves under toward the gills. The cuticle of the immature fungus is saffron yellow and covered with stiff, upturned brownish scales. As the cap develops the scales become larger and farther apart.

GILLS Close and not very broad. Attached to the stalk by a tooth and sometimes slightly decurrent along the stalk. At first it is pale olive yellow in color and later turns rust red.

STALK Cylindrical, long, and large. Generally curved. Often it grows narrower toward the base and is sometimes flattened by the base of other specimens. Above the ring it is white and smooth; below the ring it is covered with scales like those on the cap. Toward the base the stalk turns darker brown in color and the scales gradually become smaller.

RING Rather large. The outer surface, which originally covered the gills, is smooth. The other surface is covered with small brown scales, like those of the cap and stalk.

FLESH Yellowish in color. It has a strong odor of decaying wood.

MISTAKEN HARMLESSLY For **Armillariella** (**Armellaria**) **mellea** 61, a good fungus

Pholiota squarrosa (Scaly Pholiota)

35 PHOLIOTA MUTABILIS
(Changeable Agaric; Little Cluster Fungus)
KUEHNEROMYCES MUTABILIS

GOOD   Discard the stalk of mature specimens from the ring down. It can be dried.

HABITAT   From spring till autumn. Found on hardwood stumps, particularly alder, linden, and beech, and occasionally at some distance from the stumps. It grows in clusters, sometimes of enormous size.

CAP   Hemispherical, occasionally with a slight umbo in the center; later it becomes convex, sometimes with an umbo, albeit not greatly pronounced. From 1-3 inches in diameter. The margin is thin and at first curves under toward the gills. Later it turns out and often becomes undulate. The cuticle is reddish yellow or ginger brown; darker when moist. When the air is dry the margin becomes darker in color. It is frequently brick red in the center. As the fungus ages, the cuticle turns pale and cracks.

GILLS   Close and interspersed with smaller gills. Rather broad. Adnexed to the stalk, and sometimes slightly decurrent along it. Yellowish at first, then cinnamon, and finally rust colored.

STALK   Cylindrical and slender, curved and firm. Of the same color as the cap but paler in the zone above the ring. Below the ring it is darker and covered with dark reddish scales. Strong and full, then stuffed, and finally hollow.

RING   Of the same color as the cap. It has flocculose matter and scales. It tends to fall away, and some mature specimens lack a ring.

FLESH   Off-white in color under the cuticle of the cap; the flesh of the stalk is darker, almost rust colored. It has a faint odor of fruit or medicine. The taste is pleasant.

MISTAKEN   For the suspect **Hypholoma (Naematoloma) fasciculare** 30, which is very bitter in taste.

MISTAKEN HARMLESSLY   For the good **Armillariella (Armillaria) mellea 61.**

Pholiota (Kuehneromyces) mutabilis (Changeable Agaric)

36 PHOLIOTA CAPERATA
ROZITES CAPERATA

GOOD Discard the very hard lower part of the stalk of mature specimens.

HABITAT Summer and autumn. In conifer woodlands, especially pine and fir woods, though it is also found in hardwood forests. On dry sandy soil, and in mossy places. It grows in groups, sometimes in fairy rings.

CAP Ovoid or campanulate at first, then flattened campanulate or convex in shape, and finally plane or even concave. It often has a broad but slightly pronounced umbo in the center. From 2-5 inches in diameter. At first the margin curves under toward the gills. Later it turns back and becomes striate, with occasional cracks along the lines of the gills. The cuticle is light brown, but it turns darker when the air is damp and as the fungus ages. The cap of the immature fungus is covered with white furfuraceous matter that survives in the center even when the fungus is fully mature.

GILLS Close and interspersed with smaller gills. Not very broad and attached to the stalk. Yellow, and later ochre in color. The edge is lighter in color and serrate.

STALK Robust. Cylindrical in shape and thickening toward the base. It is often curved. It is off-white and floccose above the ring; below the ring, it is yellowish with silky violet striation. Strong and fibrous. Full.

RING Located just above the midpoint of the stalk. White with a yellow zone. Mature specimens often preserve only faint traces of the ring.

VOLVA Found around the base only in immature specimens. Delicate and filmy, it is white or yellowish in color.

FLESH Yellowish. The odor is mild, and the taste is pleasant.

Pholiota (Rozites) caperata (Gypsy Mushroom)

37 STROPHARIA AERUGINOSA (Green Agaric; Copper-Green Fungus; Verdigris Agaric)

INEDIBLE

HABITAT Summer and autumn. In woodlands and fields. It grows in grass.

CAP Ovoid at first, then campanulate, and finally convex or plane. It often has a broad but slightly pronounced umbo in the center. From 1-3 inches in diameter. The cuticle is sticky, almost glutinous to the touch and light blueish green or potato-green in color, particularly along the margin. The center is paler, often light brown or yellowish in color. As the fungus matures, the cap turns yellowish all over. Even immature specimens turn yellowish within a few hours after being picked. The cuticle can easily be removed from the flesh of the cap.

GILLS Very close and interspersed with smaller gills. Broad and only slightly attached to the stalk. Pinkish gray and then purplish gray in color. The edge is white and cottony.

STALK Cylindrical in form. It is the same color as the cap. Above the ring it is lighter in color and flecked with green; the base is also lighter in color. The entire stalk is covered with small white scales. Sticky. Hollow, but the inner surface is covered with a spongy substance that resembles soft breadcrumbs, even in color.

RING At first it is funnel-shaped, then it takes the form of a doughnut. It is blackish above; underneath it is white with wooly threads. Sometimes it remains attached, fringelike, to the margin of the cap. It is not durable, and mature specimens often lack the ring.

FLESH Moist and white, or greenish yellow. The odor is sometimes pungent, as strong radish, and the taste is disagreeable.

Stropharia aeruginosa (Green Agaric)

38 CORTINARIUS PRAESTANS

GOOD It is one of the faw tasty **Cortinarii**.

HABITAT Late summer and autumn. In woodlands, though less frequent in hardwood forests. It often grows in groups of several individuals.

CAP Hemispherical, then convex, and finally expanded. From 3-10 inches in diameter. The margin at first is curved under toward the gills and is striate. Later it bends back and becomes glabrous, while the striations turn into grooves and ridges. It is brown or reddish brown in color with purple tinges that disappear as the fungus ages. It is often covered with off-white or violet warts, remains of the universal veil. It is a bit viscid and shiny when the air is damp.

GILLS Very close, thick, and broad. The edge is dentate. Interspersed with smaller gills. Attached to the stalk. At first they are pale violet in color but later turn greenish brown.

STALK Thick and short, with a bulbous base. As the stalk grows in length, the bulb becomes less thick. White and silky with violet patches, and fibrillose. Stuffed.

VEIL It exists only in immature specimens. It extends from the margin of the cap to point at which the stalk thickens. It is formed of a multitude of tiny threads which have the consistency of a cobweb and are moist to the touch. Off-white or pale violet in color. In very mature specimens brownish remains of the veil are attached to the upper part of the stalk.

FLESH Firm. Grayish or yellowish under the cuticle of the cap. The flesh of the cap has violet tinges, while that of the stalk has more reddish tinges. The odor is barely perceptible, and the taste is mild.

Good

Cortinarius praestans

EDIBLE

HABITAT   Late summer and autumn in woodlands.

CAP   Convex or campanulate at first, then expanded; sometimes it is slightly concave. From 2-6 inches in diameter. The rim curves down and inward. The surface is smooth and somewhat fibrillose; it is viscid when the air is damp. The color varies from brown to violet or purple with darker patches. When it grows in coniferous woods, the cap is darker and tends to be violet in color. In hardwood farests it is lighter in color, tending toward light brown. When the fungus ages or is dried, the color fades.

GILLS   Very close and rather broad and thick. Barely attached to the stalk. Violet at first, then brownish-purple. When rubbed with the fingers the gills turn purple.

STALK   Cylindrical and squat. In conifer forests the bulb of the base becomes onion-shaped; it hardwood forests, the bulb takes the shape of a leek or does not swell at all. Light violet in color, but turning purplish when bruised. It is striate and full.

VEIL   In immature specimens, the veil extends from the margin of the cap to the base of the stalk. It is formed of a multitude of cobwebby threads, moist to the touch and violet-purple in color. Later the threads thin out and finally dry up around the stalk.

FLESH   Compact and moist. The flesh is violet; that of the stalk is darker in tone. The color fades as the fungus ages. It has a slight characteristic odor and a pleasant taste.

Cortinarius purpurascens (Purplish Cortinarius)

GOOD   It can be dried and is aromatic.

HABITAT   June and July. Upland in hardwood and conifer forests. It grows in rows or circles.

CAP   Hemispherical at first, then plane, and occasionally depressed at the center. From 2-3 inches in diameter. At first the margin curves down and under toward the gills; later it turns back and curls upward. The cuticle is dry and cracks easily, forming strips. Cinnamon in color, the margin is light violet at first; later it becomes deep cinnamon.

GILLS   Close and thin, and attached to the stalk. Very pale violet in color at first, then ochre to cinnamon.

STALK   Short and squat with a bulbous base. Pale gray violet at first, turning to pale cinnamon. Covered with rust-colored threads, the remains of the veil.

FLESH   Firm and white, with a pleasant odor and taste.

Good

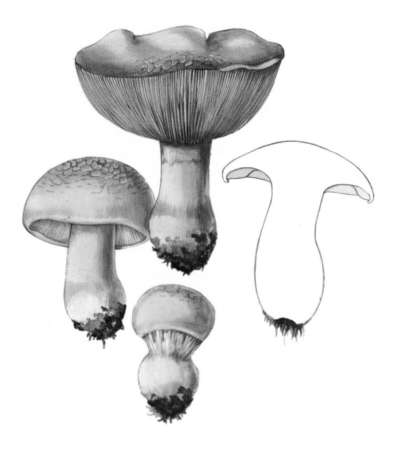

Cortinarius firmus

POISONOUS It has caused serious poisonings.

HABITAT Spring and summer. In hardwood forests, fields, along footpaths, and in parklands.

CAP Conical at first, then irregularly expanded. It almost always has a pointed cusp in the center. From 1-3½ inches in diameter. The thin margin is subdivided into irregular lobes. As the fungus matures, the margin cracks along the lines of the gills below. The cuticle is white, grayish-white, off-white, or ochre-white; later it becomes reddish brown. Dry, fibrillose, and silky.

GILLS Close and interspersed with smaller gills. Not very broad and either free from or only barely attached to the stalk. Off-white or pink at first, then olive to brown with reddish patches. The edge is white and floccose.

STALK Cylindrical and often irregular in shape. Sometimes it is thicker toward the base and the cap. Slightly bent, it is white or pale white in color with reddish patches in the mature fungus. The upper part is covered with furfuraceous matter. Fibrillose and striate, with faint traces of the veil. Full.

FLESH Firm and white, it later turns pinkish, particularly the flesh of the stalk. A light fruity odor and a pleasant taste.

MISTAKEN For other **Inocybes**, equally poisonous or suspect.

Inocybe Patouillardii (Red-Staining Inocybe)

42 ENTOLOMA LIVIDUM
RHODOPHYLLUS SINUATUS

(Leaden Entoloma)

POISONOUS   It has caused serious, if not fatal, poisonings.

HABITAT   Summer and autumn. In less dense hardwood farests, particularly oak and beech. This fungus is most frequently found around the edges of forests and woods. It grows in groups, frequently in circles. There are two or three specimens growing from a single base.

CAP   Irregularly convex at first, then expanded, flat or concave, with irregular undulation. Sometimes there is a broad but only slightly raised umbo in the center. From 2½-6 inches in diameter. The margin curves down and under toward the gills at first and is covered with whitish furfuraceous matter. Later the margin turns back and radial cracks appear. The cuticle is pale yellowish-gray, or pale greenish-gray, with leaden gray zones. Dry to the touch. Covered with flocculose matter at first, it later become glabrous. It is covered with fine fibrils between which the cuticle appears bright silver in color.

GILLS   Close and interspersed with smaller gills. They are particularly close near the margin of the cap. Unequal in length. The edge is serrate, and the gills are attached to the stalk. Pale yellowish in color, turning flesh pink and finally reddish brown.

STALK   Robust. At first the base is squat and the stalk grows thinner toward the top. Later the stalk is roughly cylindrical in shape. It is often curved at the base. White in color. The part near the gills is covered with fine furfuraceous matter at first and later with white tufts. The rest of the stalk is covered with fine brownish furry matter that later turns yellowish. Hard and full, turning spongy or sunken later.

FLESH   Solid and white turning pale yellow where it has been eaten by larvae. It has a strong farinaceous odor that becomes repugnant later. The taste is distasteful.

MISTAKEN   For the excellent **Agaricus campestris** 24, which has a ring. Mistaken for the excellent **Clitopilus prunulus** 43, which has decurrent gills along the stalk. Mistaken for the excellent **Lyophyllum Georgii** 60, which has white or off-white gills.

Entoloma lividum (Leaden Entoloma)
Rhodophyllus sinuatus

EXCELLENT Cooks quickly and can be dried.

HABITAT Summer and autumn. It grows along the edge of woods and in clearings and shady meadows. It is found chiefly under oak trees.

CAP Regular convex at first, then plane, and finally almost funnel-shaped. From 1-5 inches in diameter. The thin margin curls under at first, toward the gills; later it turns back and is irregularly undulate. The cuticle feels like suede to the touch; it is viscid when the air is damp. It is white or pale gray and covered with furfuraceous matter that falls off, although some remains along the margin.

GILLS Close and interspersed with smaller gills. Not broad. Decurrent along the stalk. The gills can be removed in clumps from the cap. Whitish at first, they turn pink and then brownish pink in color.

STALK Cylindrical and narrowing toward the gills, but squat toward the base. Rather large and often curved. The stalk is often oblique to the cap. White in color with longitudinal striation. The upper part is covered with fine furfuraceous matter, while the base is cottony. The stalk is soft.

FLESH Tender, fragile and white. It has an odor of flour. The floury taste, however, sometimes turns bitter.

MISTAKEN For the poisonous **Clitocybe dealbata** 67, which is fibrous. If one breaks the stalk of **Clitocybe dealbata** it comes apart in long fibers.

Clitopilus prunulus (Plum Agaric)

EDIBLE   Discard the fibrous stalk.

HABITAT   Summer and autumn. In shady woods, along footpaths, in grassy and mossy places. On moist soil. The Common Laccaria grows in groups of several individuals.

N. B.   All the parts of this fungus - cap, gills, stalk, and flesh - are the same color. This color varies. Most commonly it is violet, orange, or brownish orange. The color is brighter when the air is damp. It is often found lying flat on the ground, and this is its typical condition. Others are **Laccariae** of the variety **amethystina**.

CAP   Convex and depressed in the center, later becoming plane and slightly or irregularly concave at the center. From 3/4-2½ inches in diameter. The thin margin is undulate and sometimes lobed. The cuticle is smooth but later, as it dries, it becomes furfuraceous and scaly.

GILLS   Distant and interspersed with smaller gills. Broad and thick. Adnexed to and sometimes a bit decurrent along the stalk. When the fungus is mature the gills are covered with fine white furfuraceous matter.

STALK   Cylindrical and often enlarged at the base. Slender and sometimes curved. The stalk is slightly paler than the rest of the fungus. The base is white and cottony. Tenacious, fibrous, and full at first, but later sunken and hollow.

FLESH   Lean. The flesh of the stalk is fibrous, while that of the cap is tender. Faint odor and taste.

MISTAKEN HARMLESSLY   For the edible **Mycena pura** 50, which does not have decurrent gills and almost always has an umbo on the cap.

Laccaria laccata (Common Laccaria)

EDIBLE WITH CAUTION   The mature fungus may cause some disturbance, albeit not dangerous.

EDIBLE   When the fungus is immature. Care should be taken because the mature, seasoned and changed fungus may appear at first sight to be fresh and whole.

HABITAT   From late spring till autumn. In hardwood forests, particularly oak and beech. It grows on tree stumps in clusters. The bases of the individual fungi grow together.

CAP   Convex, then expanded with irregular humps or swellings. From 1 1/2-4 inches in diameter. The margin often remains a bit bent under toward the gills, and it often cracks along the line of the gills. The cuticle is reddish brown, but it fades as the fungus grows older. It is often irregularly patched. Dry and shiny.

GILLS   Sub-distant and interspersed with smaller gills. Broad and veined. Joined in a ring around the stalk. The edge is rather serrate. Whitish in color with brownish patches.

STALK   The stalk is spindly and the base is elongated like a root though it often takes other strange forms. Frequently it is twisted and is always deeply grooved. The stalk is the same color as the cap, darker toward the base and lighter toward the top. It is soft, elastic, and resistent. At first it is full of a spongy substance but later it is hollow.

FLESH   Tough, elastic, and whitish. The odor and taste are barely perceptible.

Collybia fusipes (Spindle-Stem)

GOOD   Even when picked under the snow. Discard the stalk and the gelatinous layer of the cap. It should be boiled and well seasoned.

HABITAT   Autumn and winter. It grows on old hardwood stumps, particularly elm, willow, poplar, beech, and ash, as well as on supporting posts in vineyards. It grows in clusters.

CAP   Flat or convex. From 1-3 inches in diameter. The margin is lightly striate. The surface is smooth but a bit viscid in damp air. Yellow with orange tinges; darker toward the center and lighter along the margin.

GILLS   Subdistant and interspersed with smaller gills. Broad growing toward the stalk, but shorter toward the margin of the cap. Adnexed to the stalk. White at first, turning cream or pale yellow in color.

STALK   Cylindrical and slender, usually curved. It is often off-center to the cap. The base is root shaped, curving inward, and crushed by the bases of other members of the same cluster Reddish yellow above, while the rest is dark and velvety. At first it is full of a woody pith, later it is hollow.

FLESH   That of the cap is tender, while the flesh of the stem is woody. Yellow and odorless, it has a pleasant mild taste.

MISTAKEN   For the suspect **Hypholoma (Naematoloma) fasciculare** 30, which is very bitter. Mistaken for the suspect **Hypholoma (Naematoloma) sublateritium** 31, which has gills that quickly turn olive or brownish in color.

MISTAKEN HARMLESSLY   For the good **Pholiota (Kuehneromyces) mutabilis** 35, the mature gills of which are cinnamon brown in color. Mistaken harmlessly for the good **Armillariella (Armellaria) mellea** 61, which usually has a clearly visible ring and decurrent gills along the stalk. Also mistaken harmlessly for the edible **Hypholoma (Naematoloma) capnoides**, which does not have a velvety dark stalk.

Collybia (Flammulina) velutipes (Winter Mushroom)

47 MUCIDULA MUCIDA
OUDEMANSIELLA MUCIDA

EDIBLE   Inferior.

HABITAT   Summer and autumn. On the the trunk or stump of old beeches; more rarely on the trunk or stump of old birches; still more rarely on the trunk or stump of other old hardwoods. It generally grows in clusters, but sometimes as solitary specimens.

CAP   Hemispherical at first and then gradually expanded. From 1-4 inches in diameter. It has a thin margin. Mature specimens often appear corrugated in correspondence with the gills below and are sometimes lobed. Occasionally the cap splits along the lines of the gills. The cuticle is white or grayish, sometimes with olive or brownish tinges. It is moist and viscid. Gradually, as the fungus matures, the cuticle breaks up into very tiny fibrils, running from the center toward the margin, which wrinkles.

GILLS   Distant and interspersed with smaller gills. Very broad and barely touching the stalk. Pallid, then ivory or light brown in color. The edge is often a bit floccose, scaly and edged in brown.

STALK   Cylindrical and slender. Curving. Occasionally the base is enlarged or bulbous. Whitish or just slightly tan in color. It has fine longitudinal striation. At first it is covered with very fine furfuraceous matter but later becomes glabrous. Stiff and fibrous, full at first, becoming hollow.

RING   Fairly large and thin. Located just under the cap. White and striate.

FLESH   Thin and almost transparent. Soft, fibrous, and whitish. It has a mild odor and taste.

Mucidula (Oudemansiella) mucida (Clammy Agaric)

EXCELLENT   It can be dried and becomes quite aromatic. The fairy-ring mushroom can also be eaten when it has dried out naturally on the ground.

HABITAT   From spring till autumn. In fields, clearings, sandy grassy areas, and along footpaths. Open pinewoods. It grows in rings, semi-circles, or in long rows.

CAP   Conical or campanulate, then convex, and finally expanded, sometimes becoming slightly concave. It usually has a broad but only slight pronounced umbo in the center. From 3/4-3 inches in diameter. The thin margin is sometimes curved under toward the gills, evenly or unevenly. There are sometimes ridges running parallel to the gills below. The cuticle is light brown in color, but generally darker toward the center. When the air is damp, the color is brighter and the surface is viscid. When the air is dry, the color appears faded. As the fungus ages its color fades. Generally it is smooth, but sometimes it seems wrinkly.

GILLS   Distant and interspersed with smaller gills. Broad and thick. Joined by veins. Rounded towards the stalk, but free. Whitish at first, turning the same color as the cap.

STALK   Cylindrical, long, and slender. Sometimes curved. It is often bent in drying specimens. The base is slightly squat and is covered with a white cottony substance. Off-white or the same color as the cap, but paler. At first it is covered with a cottony down and later turns glabrous. Very tenacious, elastic, and full.

FLESH   Tough, almost leathery, and elastic. Off-white in color, it has a pleasant odor and taste.

MISTAKEN   For the **Marasmius collinus**, which is poisonous for some people, but this fungus is rare. Its flesh is fragile and its stalk is tender. Mistaken for the poisonous **Clitocybe dealbata** 67, which has gills that are attached.

Marasmius oreades (Fairy-ring Mushroom)

EDIBLE Excellent as a seasoning in sauces. It can be dried and preserved.

HABITAT Summer and autumn when these season are rainy. In conifer woods. On the roots of trees and grasses, on pieces of wood, and also on the ground. It grows in large groups. Thus one can gather a large number in fairly short time, notwithstanding the fact that this is a small and slender mushroom.

CAP Almost cartilaginous. Convex at first, then expanded; 1/4-3/4 inches in diameter. Smooth and then slightly rough. Light brown or copper in color.

GILLS Very distant and narrow. Rounded toward the stalk to which they are slightly attached. The color is the same as the cap.

STALK Cylindrical, slender, and smooth. The color is the same as that of the cap. Blackish toward the base. Cartilaginous, tenacious, and hollow from top to bottom.

FLESH White with the odor and taste of garlic.

Marasmius scorodonius (Garlic Marasmius)

EDIBLE Considered suspect, but without reason. Discard part of the stalk of mature specimens.

HABITAT Summer and autumn in woodlands. It grows on mossy trunks and decomposing leaves.

CAP Conical, then flattened and smooth but with an umbo. From 3/4-2 inches. Violet to red violet; lighter in dry weather.

GILLS Distant and interspersed with smaller gills. Very broad but thin. Connected by veining to each other and attached to the stalk, often only by a tooth. Pinkish white or pale whitish violet.

STALK Cylindrical and slender, but squat at the base. The stalk grows narrower toward the gills and is sometimes curved. It is the same color as the cap. But in the variety that has a light brown cap, the stalk is violet in color. Occasionally it is off-white. Ridged throughout its length by blackish-violet fibers. Rigid. Slightly sunken and stuffed with white silky filaments.

FLESH That of the cap is white; the flesh of the stalk is slightly violet. The odor is similar to that of radishes or turnips. It tastes like turnip.

MISTAKEN HARMLESSLY For the edible **Laccaria laccata** 44, which has gills attached to the stalk and somewhat decurrent and a slight cup-shaped depression rather than an umbo on the cap.

Mycena pura (Amethyst Agaric)

GOOD   In some regions it is highly prized. The film on the cap should be removed if it is viscid.

HABITAT   From the end of summer till the first snow. It grows in woods, particularly under conifers. It can be found solitary or in groups, sometimes growing in rings.

CAP   Hemispherical or campanulate or conical at first; later expanded in various forms, sometimes with an umbo in the center and small humps. From 3-5½ inches in diameter. The margin is thin and curved under toward the gills at first. Later it turns back, becomes undulate, and splits here and there along the lines of the gills. The cuticle is grayish in color, or brownish-or violet-gray, occasionally with yellow tinges. Smooth in texture, it has blackish violet fibrils radiating from the center. When the air is damp, it is viscid, but in dry weather it dries and withers.

GILLS   Subdistant and interspersed with smaller gills; broad and thick. Adnexed to the stalk by teeth. Whitish with grayish or yellowish tinges.

STALK   Cylindrical or deformed. Robust. The base is sometimes squat and irregular in form, and sometimes it is elongated in the form of a root. Smooth, striate, it is covered with furfuraceous matter above. White and usually tinged gray or yellow. Fibrous and full at first, then hollow.

FLESH   Fragile and white. Under the cuticle of the cap it is grayish or pale violet gray. The odor and taste are not noticeable.

MISTAKEN   For the deadly **Amanita phalloides** 7, which has a ring on the stalk and a volva at the base. Mistaken for the poisonous **Tricholoma pardinum** 56, which is usually larger, hardier, and squatter than **Tricholoma portentosum**.

Tricholoma portentosum (Dingy Agaric)

52 TRICHOLOMA FLAVOVIRENS
(TRICHOLOMA EQUESTRE)

GOOD   In some regions it is highly prized and sought after.

HABITAT   From the end of summer till the beginning of winter. In hardwood and conifer forests, particularly in pinewoods. On sandy ground.

CAP   Hemispherical at first, then convex, and finally plane, sometimes with irregular humps and undulate. From 1 1/2-4 inches in diameter. The margin is curved under toward the gills, at first. Later it draws back, becomes undulate and, in some places, wrinkly. The surface is an olive yellow of varying intensity. Because of the delicate small scales that cover it, the center is rust red in color and viscid. Large sections of the cuticle can be easily pulled off the cap.

GILLS   Close and interspersed with smaller gills. The edge is undulate. Toward the margin of the cap, the gills are sinuate. Free from the stalk or barely attached by a tooth. The gills are bright sulphur yellow and this color remains.

STALK   Cylindrical. The base is often squatty and may assume irregular forms. The stalk is rather short and robust. Occasionally it is curved. Sulphur yellow in color with brownish or olive veining. Fibrillose and covered with light furfuraceous matter. Full.

FLESH   Firm and white, except for the flesh immediately under the cuticle of the cap, which is yellow. If there is any odor at all, it is pleasant, as is the taste.

MISTAKEN   For the inedible **Tricholoma sulphureum** 53, which does not have scales on the cap, however, and has distant gills, as well as an unpleasant odor of gas.

Tricholoma flavovirens (Man on Horseback)

53 TRICHOLOMA SULPHUREUM   (Sulphury Agaric; Narcissus Blewit)

SUSPECT

CAP   Convex, then plane, often with a slightly pronounced umbo in the center. Sometimes, however, the center is repressed. From 1-3¼ inches in diameter. The surface is bright sulphury yellow, often tinged with brown toward the center. Glabrous and dry, not viscid.

GILLS   Subdistant. Broad and thick. Attached to the stalk by a tooth. Sulphury yellow.

STALK   Cylindrical and occasionally squat at the base. Tall and slender, sulphury yellow. With longitudinal striation. Fibrous. Full at first, then hollow.

FLESH   Yellow or pale greenish yellow. Fibrous. Strong gassy odor or smell of sulphur dioxide.

MISTAKEN   For the good **Tricholoma flavovirens** 52, which often has a viscid cap and close gills; it is almost odorless.

Tricholoma sulphureum (Sulphury Agaric)

GOOD It cooks in an hour.

HABITAT From the end of summer till the beginning of winter. In conifer woods, and along grassy footpaths. It is gregarious and sometimes grows in rings.

CAP Conical or campanulate with an umbo in the center. It later becomes convex and finally expands, usually preserving a slightly pronounced umbo in the center. From 1-3 inches in diameter. The margin is thin and sometimes cracked. And sometimes it is lobate, the lobes being separated by cracks running parallel to the gills below. The surface is gray, brownish or darkish gray. It is usually darker toward the center. The cap is covered with small fibrous scales, dry and silky, and darker in color.

GILLS Subdistant and interspersed with smaller gills. The edge is dentate. Broad and thick. Attached to the stalk by a tooth. Fragile and whitish, turning grayish.

STALK Cylindrical. White or grayish, turning brownish toward the base. Sometimes immature specimens have a kind of veil of grayish filaments extending from the upper part of the stalk to the margin of the cap. These filaments look like parachute cords. Fragile and full, the upper part curves in.

FLESH Firm but fragile. The flesh of the cap is ashy gray, while that of the stalk is whitish. The odor and taste are barely perceptible.

MISTAKEN For the poisonous **Tricholoma pardinum** 56, which is squatter and more voluminous than **Tricholoma terreum**.

Tricholoma terreum (Gray Agaric)

EDIBLE But mediocre. To make it palatable, it should be boiled for about ten minutes and then cooked with proper seasoning.

HABITAT Summer and autumn. In hardwood, particularly oak, forests. It sometimes grows in groups of two or three.

CAP Hemispherical, then convex, and finally plane. From 2½-5 inches in diameter. The margin is tightly rolled under toward the gills. Later it withdraws a bit and forms ridges parallel to the gills below. The cuticle is yellowish white in color, or pale ochre, light brown, or pinkish brown. The center is darker in color.

GILLS Close and interspersed with smaller gills. Fairly broad and barely attached to the stalk by a tooth. Sometimes, however, they are more closely adnexed to the stalk. White or cream. They turn reddish when bruised.

STALK Cylindrical and squat. Occasionally it is even squatter at the base. White or pale ochre. The upper part is covered with lemon-yellow flocculose matter.

FLESH Firm and white. The odor is faint. The taste is generally bitter or very bitter, but it can also be pleasant and mild.

Tricholoma acerbum (Bitter Agaric)

POISONOUS It causes violent gastro-enteritis.

HABITAT Summer and autumn. In mountainous regions. In fir and beech woods; open pinewoods.

CAP Conical or campanulate in form, albeit with irregularities; then it expands, but its form remains irregular and humped. From 2½-8 inches in diameter. The thin margin is curled under at first, toward the gills. Later it withdraws and becomes undulate and lobed. It is ashy gray or whitish in color, with a slight violet tinge. It is completely covered with floccose scales that are darker in color and are broad, thin, and dry.

GILLS Close and interspersed with smaller gills. Broad and thickish, the gills are attached to the stalk only by a tooth. Cream or pale creamy yellow in color, with olive or brownish tinges. Immature specimens exude a dewy juice.

STALK Thick, it often takes the shape of a goatskin bottle. The irregularly shaped stalk is white above, paler halfway down, and slightly ochraceous toward the base. The section just beneath the gills exudes watery dewlike juice. Covered with delicate striation and down. Solid and full.

FLESH Solid and white. The flesh of the cap has grayish tinges, while that of the base of the stalk has ochraceous, or pinkish yellow tinges. The odor and taste are farinaceous, slight, and pleasant.

MISTAKEN For the good **Tricholoma portentosum** 51, which is smaller and more delicate than **Tricholoma pardinum** and grows in more numerous groups. Mistaken for the good **Tricholoma terreum** 54, which is smaller and more slender than **Tricholoma pardinum**, and has smaller and more numerous scales on the cap.

Tricholoma pardinum (Gray Tricholoma)

57 HEBELOMA CRUSTULINIFORME

SUSPECT

HABITAT Summer and autumn. In hardwood and conifer forests. On heaths, along hedges, and in gardens. It grows in groups, often arranged in rings.

CAP Hemispehrical or campanulate at first, turning gradually plane, but it sometimes maintains a strikingly cuspidate form. From 1-4½ inches in diameter. At first the margin curls under toward the gill; later it withdraws. The surface is glabrous and, in damp weather, sticky. The color varies from pale brown to pale reddish brown; this center is darker.

GILLS Very close and varying in breadth. Thin and interspersed with smaller gills. Attached to the stalk by a tooth or uncinate. Whitish at first, they turn smoky brown. The edge is dentellate, floccose, and paler. Particularly in young specimens, when the weather is damp, the gills exude milky juice which turns into tiny globules when they dry.

STALK Cylindrical with a very bulbous base. Solid and whitish. At first it is covered with furfuraceous or flocculose matter, particularly in the upper part. Later it is covered with stiff sharp points formed by bundles of outer fibers that break and turn outward. Full, gradually hollowing from top to bottom.

FLESH Watery and whitish. The odor resembles that of a turnip. The taste is unpleasant at first and turns bitter.

Hebeloma crustuliniforme (Ring Agaric)

GOOD WITH CAUTION   When raw it may cause some disturbances. It should only be eaten cooked. It is sometimes cultivated in Europe.

HABITAT   From spring to late autumn. It seems to spring up after periods of colder temperature, particularly in the autumn. In woods, particularly under conifers. On dead leaves and conifer needles. It grows in rows of several individuals; the rows are more or less arced. If one finds one specimen, one should look in the grass for others, because it is not solitary.

CAP   Convex and then plane, and finally somewhat depressed. Sometimes, however, it has a broad and slightly pronounced umbo in the center. From 2½-6½ inches in diameter. The margin is curled under at first toward the gills and is covered with fine furfuraceous matter. Later it expands, becomes undulate, and develops creases or grooves. A characteristic form of the cap groove looks like the spout of a coffee pot. This form occurs when blades of grass have interfered with the normal expansion of the cap. The surface is violet or grayish violet with brown patches, particularly toward the center. As the fungus ages, the cap may turn brownish. When the air is damp, the color is brighter. The cuticle is usually moist and smooth.

GILLS   Close and thin and interspersed with smaller gills. Narrow. Attached to the stalk by a tooth, but sometimes slightly decurrent along it. The gills can be removed in clumps from the cap. Pale violet at first, turning brownish violet.

STALK   Cylindrical and curving inward toward the top. The base is squat and is often covered with a violet cottony substance. Violet or gray violet, with lighter silky fibrils. Elastic, full, fibrous, with pith at the base.

FLESH   Tender and fragile on the cap, while the flesh of the stalk is fibrous. Pale violet on the cap, but that of the stalk is lighter. As the fungus ages, the flesh fades in color. It has a strongly aromatic odor which tends to be disagreeable. The taste is pleasant.

MISTAKEN HARMLESSLY   For the edible **Cortinarius violaceus**, which is deep purple and has a velvety cap cuticle.

Lepista nuda (Great Violet Rider)

NOT RECOMMENDED Because of its disagreeable odor. This odor remains even when the mushroom has been cooked for a long time and makes it inedible. However, it is not usually considered poisonous.

HABITAT Summer and autumn. It is more frequent in mountainous regions. It grows in clearings in woods and in pastures, particularly where the grass is dense and green. It grows in large rings of numerous individuals.

CAP Convex and slightly conical at first, becoming plane with a broad low umbo in the center. From 2½-8 inches in diameter. The margin curls under toward the gills. It only withdraws when the fungus has reached full maturity, The surface is glabrous and moist. It is brownish gray in color, but lighter when the air is dry.

GILLS Close and adnexed to the stalk, later becoming decurrent along it. White at first, turning smoky.

STALK Cylindrical. The length of the stalk is usually equal to the diameter of the cap, but it sometimes is much shorter. The base is slightly bulbous and covered with a white cottony substance. Whitish in color with distinct brown fibrillose striation. Full at first of a dense substance resembling silvery silk; later it is hollow.

FLESH Spongy, off-white turning smoky. Disagreable persistent odor, but pleasant taste.

MISTAKEN For **Melanoleuca vulgaris**, which is smaller and also not recommended.

Melanoleuca grammopodia (Ring Agaric)

EXCELLENT Fresh or dried. Aromatic.

HABITAT Spring and less commonly in the summer; still rarer in autumn. In clearings or along the edge of woods; in fields, meadows, and along hedges. Particularly near elms and hawthorns. It is gregarious and often grows in rings.

CAP Hemispherical or very convex at first, it expands and takes on an irregular shape. From 2-5 inches in diameter. The margin is thick and fleshy. At first it is closely curled toward the gills, but later it withdraws somewhat and becomes undulate. Pure white or cream in color, with violet tinges at the center. It may also be sooty white, ivory, light or dark brown in color. The cuticle of the young fungus is silky, but it turns dry and shiny.

GILLS Close, thin, and interspersed with smaller gills. Narrow with an irregular edge. They are usually attached to the stalk by a tooth, but at times they are free. There are specimens that are decurrent along the stalk. White at first, they turn pale yellow with brownish tinges.

STALK Generally squat and quite long in the variety **gambosus**. The base is slightly thickened and the stalk narrows toward the cap. White or off-white with brown tinges. Compact and full.

FLESH Solid and white. Farinaceous odor and taste.

MISTAKEN For the poisonous **Inocybe patouillardii** 41, which is distinguished by a cap that turns ever more reddish in color and has a noticeable umbo in the center. The gills are broader, not as close, and when the fungus is full grown, the gills are brownish.

N. B. The fungus shown in section on the opposite page is of the variety **gambosus**. (Often sold in European markets.)

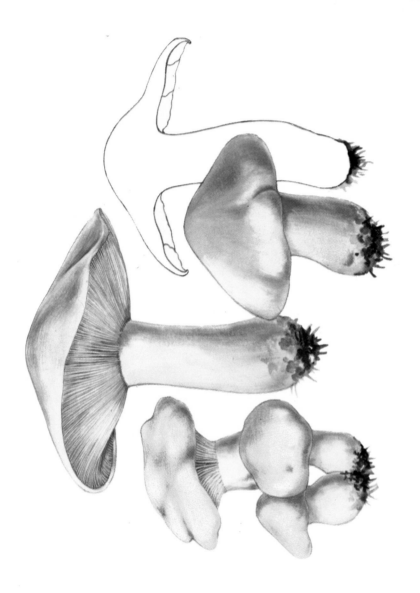

Lyphyllum Georgii (St. George's Mushroom)

61 ARMILLARIELLA MELLEA
ARMILLARIA MELLEA

(Honey Mushroom; Honey Fungus)

GOOD Discard mature specimens and part of the stalk of immature specimens. They must be thoroughly boiled, and the water in which they have been boiled should not be given as feed to animals; it can be poisonous.

HABITAT Summer and autumn. On stumps and roots of various trees, including mulberry, oak, willow, poplar, orange, fir, larch, and many others. They are very harmful to the trees on which they grow. They usually grow in numerous clusters. This mushroom rarely grows in solitary specimens, but when it does it is very large and has a bulbous base.

CAP Hemispherical or conical, then convex, or expanded. It generally has an umbo in the center. From 1½-4 inches in diameter. The margin is thin and at first is curled under toward the gills. In mature specimens it is usually a bit undulate, and the striation runs parallel to the gills. The color varies according to the tree on which the fungus vegetates: cinnamon yellow on poplar; honey colored on mulberry; yellowish brown on oak; reddish brown on conifers. On other plants it may be olive in color. It is often a bit viscid and covered with stiff pointed scales. As the fungus matures, the scales fall off.

GILLS Very close, interspersed with smaller gills. They are not very broad and grow narrower toward the margin of the cap and toward the stalk. Somewhat decurrent along the stalk. Whitish with yellowish or reddish tinges, and finally spotted reddish all over.

STALK Cylindrical and long. The base is curved and often bulbous, though often squashed by the bases of other specimens. Above the ring it is yellowish or pink and striate; below the ring it is brownish and fibrillose; the base is almost black. Tenacious, elastic, and fibrous. It is full of fibrous pith at first and later becomes hollow.

RING Thick. In young specimens it adheres to the cap margin at first and later remains facing upward. It is persistent. The upward surface is whitish and striate; the downward face is floccose and often yellowish in color.

FLESH Firm and whitish. Fibrous and tough, particularly the flesh of the stalk. The odor is slightly disagreeable or absent. The taste may be slightly bitter or acid.

MISTAKEN For the inedible **Hypholoma (Naematoloma) fasciculare** 30, which is ringless or at most preserves only a trace of the ring and is very bitter. Mistaken for the suspect **Hypholoma (Naemotoloma) sublateritium** 31, which has a brick red cap and no ring.

MISTAKEN HARMLESSLY For the good **Pholiota (Kuehneromyces) mutabilis** 35, the good **Collybia (Flammulina) velutipes** 46, and the edible **Hypholoma (Naematoloma) capnoides**, none of which has a ring.

Armillariella (Armillaria) mellea (Honey Mushroom)

62 ARMILLARIELLA IMPERIALIS
ARMILLARIA IMPERIALIS

EDIBLE But hard and indigestible when fresh. It is very good when preserved in oil.

HABITAT Late summer and autumn. In fir forests. On limely soil. It grows in the ground and frequently all that one can see is part of the surface above ground Gregarious.

CAP Convex turning plane. From 4-6 inches in diameter. The margin is smooth and curls in the shape of the volute of an Ionic capital. Later it withdraws somewhat but not entirely. It becomes undulate and cracks parallel to the gills below. Dark or light chestnut in color or olive-chestnut. The cuticle is dry, fibrillose, and somewhat peeling in the center.

STALK Very short and very thick. It is striate and narrows toward the base. It is semi-scaly. Whitish with brownish patches or pale ochre with darker patches. Hard and full.

RING There are two clearly separated rings on this fungus. The higher one is more developed. Both turn upward toward the cap. They are white in color with smoky tinges.

FLESH Hard, juicy, and white. The odor is farinaceous, and the taste is that of bitter fruit.

Armillariella (Armillaria) imperialis

GOOD   Except for the lower part of the stalk, which is hard.

HABITAT   Summer and particularly in rainy autumns. In woods and grassy areas. Gregarious, it usually grows in large rings.

CAP   Convex with a central umbo, then plane, and finally depressed and funnel-shaped, almost always preserving the umbo in the center. From 2-6 inches in diameter. The margin is thin, curled under toward the gills at first, but later uncurled. Dry, glabrous, and silky, or scaly with fine floccose matter. Pale brown or pinkish brown, and sometimes brown in color.

GILLS   Very close. Broad. Sinuate toward the cap margin and toward the stalk. Decurrent for some distance along the stalk. White, turning a lighter color than the cap.

STALK   In the shape of a truncated cone. Thick with a squat, almost bulbous base, and covered with a cottony substance, which is white in color. White at first, turning a color lighter than the cap. Elastic and full, becoming spongy.

FLESH   Solid with the same color as the rest of the fungus. The flesh of the lower part of the stalk is lighter in color. The odor resembles wild mint or lavender or honey. The taste is mild or absent.

Clitocybe geotropa (Trumpet Agaric)

64 CLITOCYBE OLEARIA (CLITOCYBE ILLUDENS)

POISONOUS It causes violent diarrhea and or nausea.

HABITAT Autumn and winter. It grows on stumps of olive, oak, and other hardwood trees. It grows in clusters.

CAP Convex, then plane, and finally depressed and somewhat funnel-shaped. The form of the cap is often altered by the pressure of other members of the same cluster. From 2½-5 inches in diameter. The margin curves under toward the gills. The cuticle is lightly marked by fibrils radiating from the center. Smooth, glabrous, and shiny. Yellow-orange or orange in color, often with brownish-red patches, later turning brown. This fungus is altogether brownish red when it grows on olive stumps.

GILLS Close and interspersed with smaller gills. Occasionally split longitudinally. Not broad, and very decurrent along the stalk. Golden yellow or varying intensities of orange. Sometimes they glow in the dark.

STALK Cornucopia-shaped and very long. The stalk grows more slender toward the base. It is often off-center to the cap. It is the same color as the cap and sometimes has darker, brownish patches. It is darker toward the base. It has longitudinal striation and is somewhat ridged. Tough, full, and fibrous.

FLESH Tough, fibrous, and yellow, varying from pale yellow to orange. The flesh of the stem is darker. The odor is strong and the taste is faint.

Clitocybe olearia (Jack O'Lantern)

65 CLITOCYBE GIBBA
(CLITOCYBE INFUNDIBULIFORMIS)

(Funnel Agaric; Funnel-shaped Clitocype; Slender Funnel Fungus)

EDIBLE Until the fungus is fully mature. It must cook for a long time and be heavily seasoned. It can be dried.

HABITAT Summer and autumn, when the weather is rainy. It grows in mountains and plains. In woods, chiefly under conifers, along the edge of woodlands, and in pastures. In grassy places. Gregarious, it grows in long rows.

CAP Plane to convex at first, becoming funnel-shaped and almost always preserving a small umbo at the center. From 1-4 inches in diameter. The margin is thin. At first it curves under toward the gills but later withdraws. It is often undulate and divided into lobes. It is covered with a fine down and has fainter undulation in the form of grooves running parallel to the gills below. The cuticle is fibrillose and silky, soon turning glabrous. Nut or ochre brown in color or, more rarely, off-white, it soon fades.

GILLS Close and interspersed with smaller gills. Narrow and strongly decurrent along the stalk. White or off-white in color.

STALK Cylindrical and slender. The base is swollen and surrounded by white cottony matter. The color is the same as or lighter than that of the cap. Darker specimens have brown fibrils. Tough, elastic, full, fibrous, and later spongy.

FLESH Delicate and elastic. White. The characteristic odor is reminiscent of bitter almonds. The taste is somewhat harsh.

Clitocybe gibba (Funnel Agaric)

GOOD But some people find it unpleasant because of its aroma. It should be boiled first to remove the odor. It can be dried.

HABITAT From the end of August till the end of November, particularly in the latter part of this period. In woods and grassy clearings. Among leaves and plant detritus. Gregarious, it grows in large groups arranged in ample rings.

CAP Convex with humps, becoming plane and even depressed into goblet shape. From 2½-8 inches in diameter. The thin margin curves under at first, then withdraws. It usually becomes somewhat undulate. At first the cuticle is covered with a fine furfuraceous matter, white in color, that easily comes away. Later it becomes glabrous, smooth, and bright. Ashy or pale brownish gray in color, but paler along the margin and darker at the center. It fades somewhat when the air is dry for long periods.

GILLS Close and interspersed with smaller gills. Narrow and somewhat decurrent along the stalk. They are easily removed from the flesh of the cap. Ashy cream in color, they become faded or yellowed as the fungus reaches maturity.

STALK Cylindrical and rather squat. It grows even squatter from the middle of the stalk down. The base is very bulbous and covered with a white cottony substance. Whitish, grayish, or pale brown in color. Elastic, full, fibrous, and spongy, later becoming more or less hollow.

FLESH Firm at first, becoming soft. White and a bit fibrous. The odor is complex with something of fresh flour about it. The taste is slightly sour.

MISTAKEN For the poisonous **Entoloma lividum** 42, which is distinguished by yellow gills that turn pink and are not decurrent.

Good

Clitocybe nebularis (Clouded Agaric)

POISONOUS   Like **Amanita muscaria** 2.

HABITAT   Summer and autumn. In fields, pastures, grasslands, open woodlands, parks; in grass and among dead leaves. It grows in numerous groups and often in clusters.

CAP   Slightly convex or plane, becoming depressed and sometimes funnel-shaped. From 3/4-3 inches in diameter. The thin margin curves down. As the fungus grows the margin turns back although it may remain slightly curved along the edge of the gills. It often wrinkles parallel to the gills beneath. At first the cuticle has a white veil-like covering. As the fungus matures this veiling gradually dissolves revealing the ashy yellow color beneath. In the end, as the fungus dries, the surface breaks up and forms scales that look like irregular spots on a creamy ochre ground.

GILLS   Close, attached to the stalk, and somewhat decurrent. Off-white or pale yellow in color.

STALK   Cylindrical, sometimes rather long. At times, however, it is quite short and squat. It is frequently narrower toward the base and incurving toward the cap. The stalk is often curved. White or off-white in color, one side or at least some patches are light brown. Tough, full, and fibrous; later quite sunken.

FLESH   Very fibrous. Very tough. White or pale. Strong mixed odor, something like that of flour. Mild taste.

MISTAKEN   For the excellent **Marasmius oreades** 48, which has gills that are not decurrent along the stalk. Mistaken for **Clitopilus prunulus** 43, which is excellent and is distinguished by its tender and fragile flesh, while the **Clitocybe dealbata** has tough flesh and gives off a strong mixed odor, similar to that of flour. **Prunulus** has a farinaceous smell as well, but it is distinctly different. Mistaken for the good **Hygrophorus niveus** 98, and for the good **Hygrophorus chrysodon** 99, which have distant gills that are fairly thick and acquire a waxy appearance with age.

N. B.   The group illustrated below on the opposite page is of the variety **rivulosa**, which is as poisonous as the variety **dealbata**.

Clitocybe dealbata (Sweat-Producing Clitocybe)

68 LEPISTA INVERSA
CLITOCYBE INVERSA

GOOD

HABITAT   Autumn. In woods, chiefly under conifers. Gregarious.

CAP   Convex with a hollow in the center, later expanded into funnel shape. From 2-4 inches in diameter. The margin is curved toward the gills at first, but later withdraws and becomes undulate. The surface is glabrous and the color is brown-red.

GILLS   Close and interspersed with smaller gills. Narrow and decurrent. Off-white or pale brownish-yellow, or tinged with orange; later turning brownish.

STALK   Cylindrical, occasionally growing slenderer toward the cap and some-what bulbous at the base. Sometimes, however, the center part is swollen. It is often bent. Very slender and a bit paler than the cap. Striate. The base is covered with white cotton. Full and spongy, becoming hollow as far as the point just below the cap cuticle.

FLESH   Fragile, off-white, turning pale pinkish brown or pale brown. It has no characteristic odor, and the taste is rather sour.

Lepista (Clitocybe) inversa (Brown-red Clitocybe)

GOOD As long as it is immature. Discard the stalk and base of the cap. It requires long cooking.

HABITAT Spring and fall; wet summers when not too hot. On hardwood stumps and trunks, as well as on timber detritus exposed to the elements. More rarely on conifer stumps and trunks. It grows in clusters of numerous individuals.

CAP It is shaped like a horseshoe or a fan or a seashell. From 2-6 inches in diameter. The caps of the same cluster overlap like roofing tiles; close together and rising in several layers. The color varies from white to pale brownish gray, to brownish gray, brown, or deep purple. The color fades as the fungus matures. The inner part of a cap below another specimen may be covered by a light coating of cottony matter, whitish in color, that becomes felty when dried.

GILLS Very close, unequal, often branching and very broad. Somewhat decurrent along the stalk. Cream color, turning off-white.

STALK Hidden by the cap and growing together with the stalks of other members of the same cluster. Large. Sometimes absent, usually short, it may occasionally be quite long. It narrows toward the cap and is attached from the side, not from below. White, it often has down covering the base. Firm and full.

FLESH Tender in young fungi; tough in mature specimens. White with a faint odor of flour. Pleasant taste.

Pleurotus ostreatus (Oyster Mushroom)

EXCELLENT   It can be dried. It makes an excellent garnish and seasoning.

HABITAT   Spring and autumn. It grows in summer as well, if the season is not excessively dry. It grows on the roots of various species of spiny umbelliferous plants, similar to thistles, such as the **Eryngium campestre** and the **Eryngium maritimum**. In fields, along roads, in sandy places. It is common in southern Italy. The white **Pleurotus nebrodensis**, which is excellent for eating, grows in the Alps.

CAP   Convex, then plane or depressed, it is occasionally concave. Its form is usually very irregular. From 1½-5 inches in diameter. The margin curves toward the gills, but later withdraws and expands, usually forming irregular lobes and becomes undulate, sometimes growing in fantastic shapes. The surface is covered with small scales at first but soon becomes glabrous and shiny. Brownish gray in color, it fades as the fungus ages and sometimes turns off-white in color.

GILLS   Not close, unequal, and fairly narrow. Decurrent along the stalk. White turning pale pink, pale pinkish gray, or pale brownish gray.

STALK   Cylindrical, growing narrow toward the cap. It is occasionally squatty at the base, though generally coming to a point. Sometimes it is central to the cap but more often it is slightly off-center. White or off-white, smooth, glabrous, solid and full.

FLESH   Tender, dry, and white. The odor is mild and pleasant, and the taste is delicate.

Excellent

Pleurotus eryngii

71 PLEUROTUS FUSCUS var. FERULAE LANZI

EXCELLENT   It can be dried and makes for fine seasoning or garnish.

HABITAT   Autumn. On the roots of various Mediterranean umbelliferous plants, such as the **Ferula**.

CAP   Convex turning plane-depressed. The form is usually quite irregular. From 1 1/2-3 1/2 inches in diameter. The margin curls under toward the gills and is slightly undulate. Smoky gray in color, turning yellowish gray.

GILLS   Not close, rather narrow, and decurrent and slightly branching along the stalk. Pale yellowish gray.

STALK   The form resembles that of a goatskin bottle. Solid. The base is carrot-shaped. Off-white and full.

FLESH   Firm and white. It has a mild odor when fresh and becomes aromatic when dried. It has a delicate flavor.

Pleurotus fuscus var. ferulae lanzi

GOOD

HABITAT Summer and autumn. In hardwood forests. On old trunks, particularly oak and elm. It grows in clusters.

CAP Convex, becoming expanded or depressd. Finally it assumes an often irregular funnel shape. From 2-5 inches in diameter. At first it is covered with a fine down, but it soon becomes glabrous. White or off-white, frequently with pink tinges, finally turning ochre-yellow.

GILLS Neither very close, nor very broad. Interspersed with smaller gills. Decurrent and branching out netlike along the stalk. White, becoming tinged with pink.

STALK Cylindrical and usually quite off-center to the cap. It is frequently curved and joins the bases of other specimens in the same cluster. Velvety and white.

FLESH Soft and white. The odor is farinaceous and the taste is mild.

Good

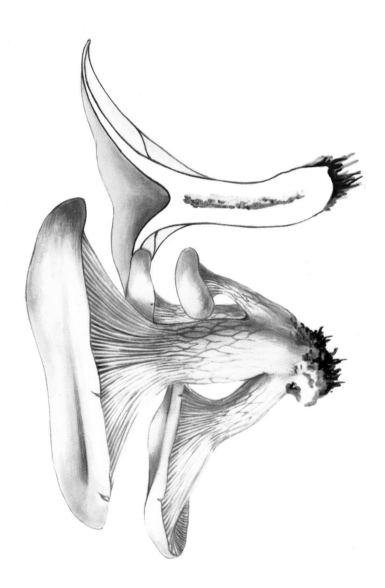

Pleurotus cornucopiae

73 LENTINELLUS COCHLEATUS
LENTINUS COCHLEATUS

EDIBLE But only if totally immature, although even the young fungus is hard and not easily digested.

HABITAT Summer and autumn. In woodlands, particularly in beech woods. It grows on tree stumps in large clusters many of which are joined by the cap.

CAP Ear- or funnel-shaped, open on one side with one end curled like a ram's horn inside the other. From 1-4 inches in diameter. Thin and elastic. The edge is cracked and forms undulate lobes. It is curled under toward the gills. Reddish brown or reddish ochre in color, but fading when the air is dry and as it ages. The surface is often quite wrinkled.

GILLS Very close and unequal; not very broad. The edge is irregularly serrate. Decurrent along the stalk almost to the base. Whitish at first, then turning pinkish.

STALK The lower part of the fungus may be considered a stalk even though it forms a continuous whole with the cap. It looks like a twisted inverted cone and is deeply grooved. Usually it is not central to the cap but off-center or even lateral to it. The same color as the cap but sometimes darker. Hard, stuffed, and fibrous.

FLESH Thin, cartilaginous, tough, and reddish. The odor resembles anise or lavender, but it vanishes quickly. Almost tasteless.

Lentinellus (Lentinus) cochleatus (Shell Lentinellus)

GOOD   Even raw. It should be cooked slowly, on a grill over an open fire, in a frying pan or baked; it will dissolve in liquid. It requires abundant seasoning.

HABITAT   Particularly in the summer but also in the autumn. In hardwood and conifer forests, and in damp caves and grottoes. It is usually solitary.

CAP   Convex with the margin curved down toward the gills at first, becoming expanded and depressed or funnel-shaped. If often has humps. From 2-6 inches in diameter. The margin gradually withdraws and becomes undulate. As the fungus ages, the surface of the cap cracks. It is light orange-brown, light cinnamon-brown, or reddish brown in color, frequently with darker patches particularly toward the center. Smooth and dry, it is not shiny.

GILLS   Close near the margin of the cap but distant toward the stalk. Thick and interspersed with many smaller gills. Rather narrow and slightly decurrent along the stalk. Pale cream in color, turning pale ochraceous yellow. The gills turn brown when bruised, and exude latex.

STALK   Cylindrical and occasionally squatty half-way down. A bit paler than the cap with reddish paches, chiefly toward the base; yellower toward the top. At first it is covered with fine furfuraceous matter and later it wrinkles lightly. Hard and full.

FLESH   Firm and fragile. Whitish in color. The flesh of the cap turns brownish when exposed to the air, while that of the stalk becomes marbled a pale reddish color. The flesh just below the cuticle of the stalk becomes tinged with yellow. The aroma is pleasant, but as the fungus ages, or after picking, it many take on a decidedly fishy odor which in no way alters the pleasant taste.

LATEX   Abundant and fluid. It is white and generally does not change color when exposed to the air; only exceptionally does it turn slightly yellow. It is not sour

Lactarius volemus (Orange-Brown Lactarius)

GOOD Only when very young. It should be eaten cooked, not raw. It should be prepared slowly on a grill fried in a pan or baked. It dissolves when cooked in liquid.

HABITAT Late summer and autumn. In conifer woods.

CAP Plane or convex with the margin curved under toward the gills; later it becomes expanded or depressed and occasionally concave like a goblet. It sometimes preserves a small umbo. From 2-5 inches in diameter. When the fungus is fully mature, the margin is uncurled and sinuate. The cuticle is smooth, and it is viscid when the air is damp. Bright or pale orange or ochraceous orange in color, with concentric zones sometimes noticeably darker. As the fungus ages the color fades and coppery-green patches appear until the entire fungus is this color. When bruised it turns a coppery green color.

GILLS Close and interspersed with smaller gills. Branching and decurrent along the stalk. Slightly paler than the cap.

STALK Cylindrical and often narrower toward the base. Of the same color as the cap, but frequently with patches or tinges of greenish color. The stalk bears erosion pittings that are slightly darker in color. Solid, fragile and full, but soon hollow. It is often wormy, particularly if it has aged. Covered with furfuraceous matter that gives it a pink or ochre cast.

FLESH Firm and fragile. The outer flesh is pinkish yellow but the inner flesh is lighter in color. Green under the cuticle of the cap and bright orange under the cuticle of the stalk. It turns coppery green when exposed to the air, but this color gradually diminishes. The odor is pleasantly tart, as is the taste.

LATEX Abundant and dense. Orange in color, it stains. It becomes coppery green on exposure. Not tart.

MISTAKEN For the suspect **Lactarius torminosus** 76, which exudes a white latex and has a wooly margin. The latex of a similar suspect **Lactarius** exudes white and changes to yellow.

MISTAKEN HARMLESSLY For the good **Lactarius sanguifluus,** which is distinguished, however, by its redder cap and flesh and its distinctly dark red or purple-red latex.

Lactarius deliciosus (Delicious Milk Cap)

76 LACTARIUS TORMINOSUS

SUSPECT Often reported to be poisonous, although there is some disagreement. It is best avoided.

HABITAT Summer and autumn. In woods and clearings, particularly under birches, with which it forms mycorrihiza.

CAP Plane or convex, becoming expanded or depressed, sometimes with a pit at the center or goblet- or funnel-shaped. From 3/4-4 1/2 inches in diameter. The margin is curled under toward the gills and remains curved though only at the rim, where the cuticle breaks up into a delicate fringe. Light creamy orange or light pinkish brown in color, but paler along the margin. It almost always has concentric fibrillose zones of a darker color.

GILLS Very close and interspersed with many smaller gills. Not very broad and decurrent along the stalk. Light creamy pink with pink tinges.

STALK Cylindrical and usually narrowing toward the cap. It often becomes much thinner toward the base. A bit lighter in color than the cap. Covered with fine furfuraceous matter. It often has shallow erosion pittings. Solid, fragile, and full, though soon hollow and often wormy.

FLESH Firm. White or cream-colored. Pleasant odor. The taste is slightly tart.

LATEX Abundant, white, and very tart.

MISTAKEN For the good **Lactarius deliciosus** 75, which, however, exudes an abundant orange latex that stains and turns coppery green.

Lactarius torminosus (Wooly Milk Cap)

INEDIBLE   Very sharp taste.

HABITAT   Autumn. In the mountains and in conifer woods.

CAP   Convex with a depression in the center at first; later it is goblet- or funnel-shaped. From 3-9½ inches in diameter. The margin is curled under toward the gills and resembles an Ionic volute. It withdraws only when the fungus has fully matured. It is fringed with fine dense down. Yellow or light brownish yellow in color. At first the cuticle is covered with glutinous matter that makes it sticky to the touch. Later this matter dries forming a kind of glutinous crust that covers the patches that cover much of the cap surface. This glutinous crust is darker than the general color of the cap.

GILLS   Close and interspersed with smaller gills. Slightly decurrent along the stalk. Cream-colored but the gill edges are yellowish at first, turning brown and becoming patched with reddish brown.

STALK   Cylindrical and swollen. The base is frequently curved. It is pitted with small oval or irregularly shaped depressions of a darker color. The general color of the stem is somewhat lighter than that of the cap. Solid but soon worm-eaten. Hollow, or the interior of the stalk is filled with a spongy breadlike substance.

FLESH   Hard and fragile. White but soon turning bright yellow because of the latex it exudes. Pleasant odor. The taste is mild at first but turns sharp.

LATEX   Abundant and white but turning bright yellow immediately on exposure to the air.

Lactarius scrobiculatus

SUSPECT The edibility of this mushroom is variously reported, and it is best avoided.

HABITAT Late summer and autumn. In conifer woods, particularly where vegetation is very thin. Only exceptionally does it grow in hardwood forests and then only when conifer woods are nearby. Wet places.

CAP Convex and almost conical because of a small but pronounced umbo in the center. Later it expands and becomes depressed, sometimes assuming the shape of a funnel but always preserving the central umbo. From 1-4 inches in diameter. The thin margin is curved under toward the gills, later it expands, and finally becomes somewhat irregular in shape. The cuticle is covered with fine furfuraceous matter at first. It becomes viscid when the air is damp. Brownish red in color, it does not fade when the air is dry or as the fungus ages.

GILLS Close and interspersed with smaller gills. Not very broad. Decurrent along the stalk. Ivory at first, becoming pale reddish ochre with occasional patching later the gills are covered with a fine powdery substance.

STALK Cylindrical and very long. It thickens toward the base. Reddish gray and covered with fine furfuraceous matter, but it becomes almost glabrous later. The base is paler in color and is enveloped by a white cottony substance. Full but soon stuffed with pithy matter.

FLESH Firm and fragile. Whitish in color, except for that of the stalk and that just under the cap cuticle, which is reddish. Mild odor. Very sharp taste.

LATEX White and very sharp, it produces a caustic effect on the lips as well as on the tongue.

MISTAKEN HARMLESSLY For the edible **Lactarius mitissimus**, a smaller fungus with a mild undistinguished taste.

Lactarius rufus (Red Lactarius)

EDIBLE But not recommended. If eaten raw it is quite inferior, nor is it very good cooked, for an acrid taste remains even after long boiling. In some European regions where it is prepared in oil it is prized and this treatment probably improves the fungus.

HABITAT Summer and autumn. In woods, along fields, and particularly in the vicinity of aspens. Gregarious, it often grows in large rings.

CAP Convex and depressed at first, later expanding in the form of a goblet or funnel. From 3-12 inches in diameter. In the young fungus the margin is curved toward the gills; when the fungus is fully mature the margin uncurls completely; and often becomes undulate. The cuticle of the immature fungus is covered with fine down and later remains covered with plant detritus. It is viscid when the air is damp. White in color with pink or pale reddish-violet zones, sometimes arranged concentrically.

GILLS Close and interspersed with many smaller gills. Occasionally branching. Narrow. Decurrent along the stalk. White at first, turning pink.

STALK Cylindrical or in the form of an upside-down truncated cone. Squat. Frequently it is not central to the cap but extremely off-center, sometimes it is lateral to the cap. Off-white with occasional pale violet patches. Glabrous. Hard. Full at first and often eaten away inside when the fungus is mature.

FLESH Firm and fragile. White but occasionally pink under the cap cuticle. The odor is somewhat acid and quite disagreeable. The taste is bitter turning tart.

LATEX White and tart.

MISTAKEN For **Lactarius piperatus** 81, which is edible with caution, although this variety has extremely close gills, creamy-white at first, turning yellowish in color. Mistaken for **Lactarius vellereus** 80, which is edible with caution. **L. vellereus** 80 has yellowish gills when the fungus is mature.

Lactarius controversus (Stained Lactarius)

EDIBLE WITH CAUTION   But not recommended. It is quite inferior, and disagrees with some people.

HABITAT   Summer and autumn in hardwood forests.

CAP   Convex or depressed at first, with humps. Later it becomes goblet- or funnel-shaped. From 3-10½ inches in diameter. The margin of the young fungus is curved under toward the gills; it gradually unfurls and becomes undulate. The surface is covered with fine down, which makes the surface very rough to the touch when the air is dry. White in color with yellowish, brownish, or reddish tinges.

GILLS   Not close. The gills are joined here and there by veining. Narrow but thick. Decurrent along the stalk. White with bluish-green or lemon yellow tinges, but turning yellowish and finally become patched reddish brown.

STALK   Cylindrical and narrowing toward the gills. The foot is narrower and rounded or takes the form of an upside-down truncated cone. Squat. Occasionally it is not central to the cap but quite off-center. Of the same color as the cap. Pruinose and sometimes covered with fine down like that of the cap. Hard and full.

FLESH   Hard and fragile. White but turning pale brown or greenish yellow on contact with the air. The odor is pleasant, but the taste is sharp.

LATEX   Scarce and white. The taste is very sharp.

MISTAKEN   For **Lactarius piperatus** 81, which is edible with caution and is distinguished by the smooth surface of its cap and extremely close and often branching gills.

MISTAKEN HARMLESSLY   For the edible **Russula delica** 91, which does not exude latex. Mistaken harmlessly for the inferior but edible **Lactarius controversus** 79, which is distingèuished by the pink gills of the mature fungus.

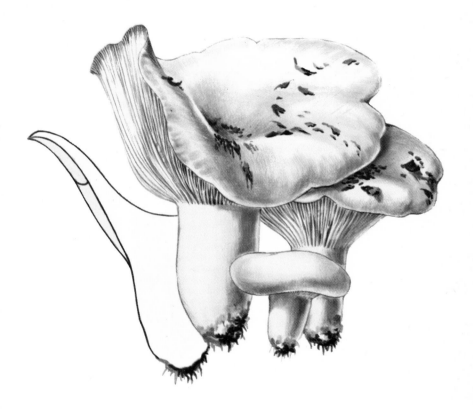

Lactarius vellereus (Wooly-white Lactarius)

EDIBLE WITH CAUTION Even when it has been parboiled and cooked, it is very bitter and difficult to digest. It turns a pale bluish green when cooked. Dried and ground it can be used in the same way as ground red pepper.

HABITAT Summer and autumn. In hardwood and coniferous forest. In shady and damp places. Gregarious, it often grows in rows or rings.

CAP Convex or depressed then becoming funnel-shaped. From 2½-6½ inches in diameter. At first the margin curls under toward the gills, but when the fungus has reached full maturity, it is completely unfurled, irregularly undulate and lobed. The surface is smooth and dry, but it cracks with age. White, it is frequently marked with ochre or reddish patches, though not along the margin, which remains white.

GILLS Very close and occasionally branching. Interspersed with smaller gills that are often attached to the larger ones. Not broad. At first adnexed to the stalk, and later decurrent along it. White in color, turning creamy white. As the fungus ages, the gills turn yellow or become covered with greenish yellow patches. Sometimes they have reddish patches of coagulated latex.

STALK Cylindrical or inverted truncated cone. Sometimes the stalk is not central but off-center to the cap. White with greenish tinges at first; later with reddish tinges. Smooth and only rarely rough. The stalk of the young fungus is covered with fine furfuraceous matter. Hard and full.

FLESH Hard and fragile. Creamy white in color, it slowly turns yellowish on contact with the air. It has no noticeable odor, but the taste is very peppery.

LATEX Abundant and sirupy. White at first, but as it dries it often turns greenish blue. Very peppery.

MISTAKEN For **Lactarius vellereus** 80, which has a down-covered cap surface that becomes slightly rough to the touch when the air is dry; it is also distinguished by its subdistant gills. **L. vellereus** 80 is edible with caution.

MISTAKEN HARMLESSLY For the edible **Lactarius controversus** 79, which has white gills turning pink. **Lactarius piperatus** never has pink gills.

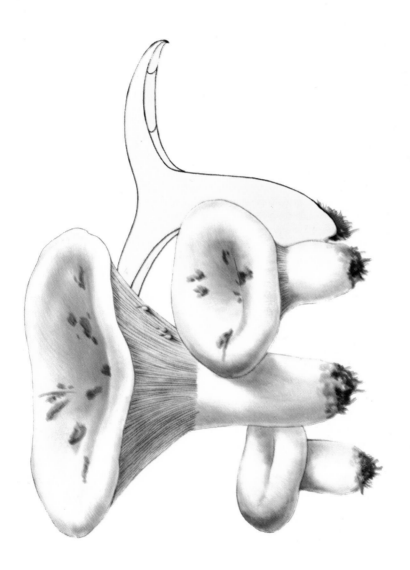

Lactarius piperatus (Pepper Cap)

GOOD When cooked immediately.

HABITAT From the end of spring till the end of summer; rarely in autumn. In hardwood forests and dark moist places.

CAP Convex, becoming plane-convex, and finally depressed with occasional humps. From 1½-3½ inches in diameter. The thin margin is grooved parallel to the gills below in the mature fungus. The cuticle is a bit viscid when the air is damp and can be removed only along the margin. It is shiny. Orange-red, coppery red, or purplsh red in color, often with lemon or golden yellow zones. Sometimes the fungus is lemon or golden yellow in color.

GILLS Very close and broad, occasionally branching. Joined by veining near the stem. Generally the gills are free from the stalk, but sometimes they just barely touch. Creamy white in color at first, then lemon yellow, and finally ochre. The edge is golden or lemon yellow.

STALK Cylindrical and narrowing toward the cap. The base is occasionally squat. White or slightly lemon yellow, particularly toward the base. With brownish patches. Fairly rough. Hard and fragile. Full, turning spongy.

FLESH Firm and fragile. White in color, but the flesh under the cap cuticle is lemon yellow. The odor is insignificant and the taste is mild.

MISTAKEN For the poisonous **Russula emetica** 82, which has a very sharp taste.

MISTAKEN HARMLESSLY For other **Russulae** with red caps, non-acrid taste and edible.

N. B. There are many red **Russulae** which are easily mistaken for one another. When in doubt, keep only those that have yellow gills from the early youth to maturity of the fungus and those that do not have a sharp taste. Those with white gills and those yellow-gilled forms that have a sharp taste should be discarded.

Russula aurata (Golden Russula)

POISONOUS   It is generally regarded as such, although a very few writers suggest that one or two of these fungi can be used as a hot seasoning mixed with other mushrooms of other species. The popular names for this mushroom, however, should stand as adequate warning against overuse.

HABITAT   Summer and autumn. In hardwood and coniferous forests. In damp and even in swampy places; near moss.

CAP   Convex, then plane, and finally depressed; sometimes perfectly concave. From 1-4 inches in diameter. The margin of the immature fungus is smooth but usually becomes grooved parallel to the gills and then knotty. The cuticle is viscid when the air is damp, and it can easily be detached from the cap in large pieces. It is bright red in color, but discolors easily and sometimes it is only pink or even white with occasional pink tinges here and there.

GILLS   Rather close depending on the variety. Frequently branching and interspersed with smaller gills. Broad and rounded toward the margin of the cap. Free from the stalk or adnexed. White, often with greenish blue or greenish yellow tinges.

STALK   Cylindrical with a base that is sometimes swollen and sometimes tapering. White with a tendency to turn yellow, particularly toward the base. Grooved with fine wrinkles. Solid, full, later empty.

FLESH   Thick or thin, resistent or fragile, depending on the variety. Spongy in the mature fungus. White with a tendency to turn yellow. The flesh under the cap cuticle is pink or blood red when the cap is bright red. Even a small taste prooves soon to be very hot and sharp, and this taste lingers for quite a while in the mouth.

MISTAKEN   For the inedible **Russula fragilis**, because of the hot taste, a smaller fungus than the **Russula emetica** and very brittle.

N. B.   There are many red **Russulae** which can easily be mistaken for one another. When in doubt keep only those that have yellow gills even in young specimens and do not have a sharp taste. Discard those with white gills and those that have yellow gills but a sharp taste.

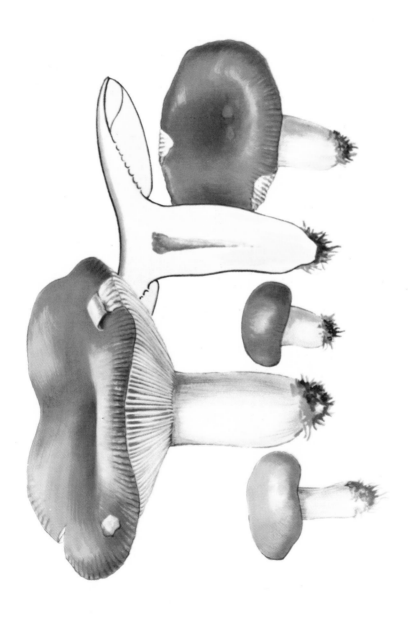

Russula emetica (Emetic Russula)

EDIBLE Not highly recommended because it is very bitter. If it is to be used, the mushroom should be parboiled for a few minutes in lightly salted water before cooking and the boiling water discarded.

HABITAT Summer and autumn. Chiefly in hardwood forests, especially oak and beech, but also in coniferous woods.

CAP Convex, often almost hemispherical, but sometimes semi-oval; later plane and very occasionally somewhat depressed. From 1½-4½ inches in diameter. The margin is smooth without striation, a bit undulate, and almost always without splitting. The cuticle is dry and covered with fine furfuraceous matter, velvety and when the air is damp a bit translucent. When the weather remains dry for long periods is splits. It is difficult to detach the cuticle from the cap. Bright vermilion in color with occasional zones, usually toward the center, that are ever intenser in color. Sometimes, however, it is marked by occasional paler, whitish or yellowish patches. The color fades when the air is dry.

GILLS Close at first, but less close in the mature fungus. Not very broad with occasional branching. Rounded toward the cap margin. Very slightly attached to the stalk. Milk-white in color with whitish-brown or greenish tinges. Sometimes the gills are pink along the edge, especially toward the cap margin. Fragile

STALK Cylindrical and short, and occasionally swollen at the base. White, usually with a pink or reddish patch along one side. Smooth and covered with furfuraceous matter. Occasionally there are some longitudinal grooves. Hard, fragile and full.

FLESH Thick and hard, almost like an apple. Fragile, granulose, and white. Raw it has a mild fruity or minty odor; when cooked it has a strong alkaline odor. The taste of the gills is a bit bitter; the rest of the fungus tastes pleasant and nutty at first, but it soon turns rather bitter also.

N. B. There are may red **Russulae** which can easily be misaken one for another. When in doubt keep only those that have yellow gills even in young specimens and do not have a sharp taste. Discard those with white gills and those that have yellow gills but a sharp taste.

Russula lepida (Scaly Russula)

85 RUSSULA VESCA

GOOD Even dried.

HABITAT From May till the end of summer; rarely in autumn. In plains and in woods, particularly larch, oak, and beech. It is rarely found in mountainous regions and only in hardwood forest.

CAP Convex, becoming plane or depressed. From 2½-4½ inches in diameter. The margin is slightly undulate, and that of the mature fungus sometimes has short grooves parallel to the gills below. The cuticle is sometimes smooth and sometimes slightly wrinkly. Viscid in damp weather, but it dries quickly and is easily detached from the flesh of the cap. Brownish-red flesh colored but darker toward the center. It may sometimes appear light brown or pale grayish brown or dirty white in color.

GILLS Close or subdistant. Broad. Often branching. Adnexed to the stalk and, when fully grown, sometimes slightly decurrent along it. In damp weather they exude drops that dry in dry weather and form yellowish spots. White in color with cream or greenish tinges.

STALK Cylindrical and often bulging. Sometimes it narrows toward the base. Rather wrinkly. White with occasional pale reddish patches. Full, then spongy and wormy.

FLESH Firm and resistent. White, it tends to turn brown. The flesh of the base is rusty in color. The odor is faint, and there is a nutty taste.

N. B. There are many red **Russulae** which can easily be mistaken one for another. When in doubt keep only those that have yellow gills even in young specimens and do not have a sharp taste. Discard those with white gills and even those with yellow gills but a sharp taste.

Russula vesca (Edible Russula)

86   RUSSULA INTEGRA

GOOD

HABITAT   Spring and summer. In mountains, rarely in the plains. In coniferous forests.

CAP   Convex, often very irregular in shape; becomes expanded or depressed and sometimes takes on an irregular saucer shape. From 2-5 inches in diameter. The margin is smooth at first, turning rather grooved, and sometimes with knobby ridges. When the fungus is full grown the margin is often turned up. The cuticle is moist, viscid, bright, wrinkly, and a good part of it can be detached. The basic color of the cap is brown but with varying tinges - yellowish brown with olive areas, chocolate brown, purplish brown, violet brown, or olive brown.

GILLS   Close at first, then distant. Interspersed with smaller gills. Occasionally branching. Rounded toward the cap margin. They only barely touch the stalk. Milk-white in color, turning creamy yellow, finally becoming yellowish.

STALK   Cylindrical and very irregular in form. White turning yellowish with brownish patches. Finely grooved. Full, then pithy, and finally hollow.

FLESH   Solid, white. The odor is mild and pleasant. It has a nutty taste.

N. B.   There are many red **Russulae** which can easily be mistaken one for another. When in doubt keep only those that have yellow gills even in young specimens and do not have a sharp taste. Discard those with white gills and even those with yellow gills when they have a sharp taste.

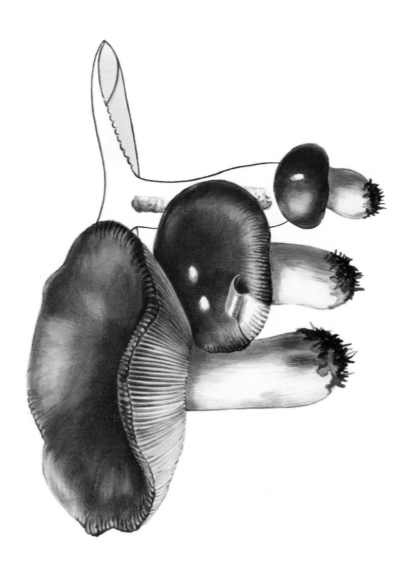

Russula integra

87 RUSSULA BADIA

POISONOUS

HABITAT Summer and autumn. In coniferous woods and on sandy ground.

CAP Convex, turning plane-convex. From 2-4 inches in diameter. The margin remains smooth for a long time, finally becoming undulate and grooved parallel to the gills beneath. The cuticle is viscid and shiny, but it soon turns dry and loses all brightness; it often is grooved with radiating striation. The basic color is red - vermillion or brownish red, but always dark, almost black toward the center. If often has occasional brighter patches.

GILLS Not very close. Rather broad. Clear yellow at first, turning ochre yellow.

STALK Cylindrical. The central part is often swelling. White with frequent purplish patches. Soon hollow.

FLESH White. The odor is similar to cedarwood. The taste is mild for a while, turning very sharp.

N. B. There are many red **Russulae** which can easily be mistaken one for another. When in doubt keep only those that have yellow gills even in young specimens and do not have a sharp taste. Discard those with white gills and even those with yellow gills when they have a sharp taste.

Poisonous

Russula badia

GOOD It is best cooked on a grill.

HABITAT Summer and autumn. In coniferous and hardwood forests.

CAP Globular, turning convex, and finally expanded, sometimes with a central pit, depressed, or goblet-shaped. From 1½-6 inches in diameter. At first the margin curls under toward the gills, but it later expands regularly or divided into broad lobes. The cuticle is viscid at first but later dries and becomes covered with fine radial grooves. It is easily detached from the flesh of the cap. The usual color is blackish purple or bluish violet, but it may also be dark coppery, dark green, green-grayish-violet in color and vary in intensity. Even when one of these shades dominates, there may be patches of one of the other shades. It is never red.

GILLS Close or almost close. Broad and rather thick. Frequently branching. Sometimes interspersed with smaller gills. Veined. Adnexed to the stalk, some-times only barely, and sometimes slightly decurrent along it. White with blue-green tinges. Flexible, almost elastic.

STALK Cylindrical or squatty toward the middle. Often very large, but some-times rather thin. Generally becoming thinner toward the base. White, occasion-ally tinged with violet. It often has brown spots and is covered with furfuraceous matter. Grooved when the fungus is full grown. Elastic. Full, then spongy, and finally hollow and wormy.

FLESH Thick, solid, and somewhat elastic. A bit granulose. Generally white, but pink under the cap cuticle and violet or brown where it has been eaten by insects. Exposed to the air, the flesh slowly turns ashy in color. It is odorless. The taste is pleasant at first, but when it is chewed it turns somewhat sharp.

MISTAKEN For the deadly **Amanita phalloides** 7, which is distinguished, however, by the ring on the stalk, the volva at the base, its numerous smaller and non-branching gills.

Russula cyanoxantha (Blue-and-Yellow Russula)

GOOD

HABITAT   Summer and autumn. In hardwood forests, especially beech, oak, and chestnut. Less frequent in coniferous woods.

CAP   Globose at first, then convex, and finally expanded; it may also be very depressed. From 2½-8 inches in diameter. The margin is curled under toward the gills at first; then it withdraws and becomes irregularly undulate and lobed. The cuticle is dry and often wrinkly; it cracks in concentric circles, but when the air is damp it becomes somewhat viscid. It can be detached from the flesh of the cap for about one third of the radius. The typical color of the cap is olive, but it may also be olive brown, violet, purplish red, or brownish red; it often has patches of other colors.

GILLS   Very close at first, becoming very distant. Occasionally branching. Veined. Broad and thick. The gills are either free or only slightly touch the stalk. Pale yellow in color, turning ochre yellow; occasionally the edge has tinges of the color of the cap.

STALK   Cylindrical. The stalk of the mature fungus often narrows and curves in toward the cap. Large and white, with frequent pink tinges, except at the base. Sometimes it is all pink. But as the fungus ages this coloring tends to vanish. Covered with fine furfuraceous matter and later with fine grooves running up and down. Hard and full, but stuffed with a spongy substance.

FLESH   Thick, firm, and resistent at first, becoming fragile. White, but turning yellowish on exposure to the air. It has a tenuous odor and a pleasant taste.

MISTAKEN HARMLESSLY   For the edible **Russula alutacea**, which is more varied in coloring, has a cuticle that can easily be detached in large sections to the mid-radius of the cap, and a margin more markedly grooved and parallel to the gills than **Russula olivacea**; it sometimes has knobby grooves. The gills of **Russula alutacea** are creamy to pale yellow then ochre yellow almost from the moment that the fungus emerges from the ground.

N. B.   There are many red **Russulae** which can easily be mistaken one for another. When in doubt keep only those that have yellow gills even in young specimens and do not have a sharp taste. Discard those with white gills and even those with yellow gills when they have a sharp taste.

Good

Russula olivacea

GOOD   Grilled or cooked in a saucepan.

HABITAT   July and August. It grows in coniferous woods but is more common in thin hardwood forests - oak, chestnut, beech, and birch. Open places. It sometimes grows on land that has been burned. Gregarious.

CAP   Ovoid or globose, then more or less compressed and irregular in shape, then convex, and finally expanded; it is often depressed and gibbose. From 2-6 inches in diameter. The margin is smooth and often irregular in shape and lobed. In the mature fungus the cap is grooved parallel to the gills beneath. The cuticle is thick, dry, and detachable from the cap up the middle of the radius. White at first with small pale brown or pale green patches. These patches turns a warmer color after a while. Later polygonal whitish cracks form around these patches, by now greenish yellow, bluish green, or brownish green in color. Sometimes these patches are very tiny and seem to be merely grains. .

GILLS   Very close and very broad. Thick and sometimes branching. Sometimes interspersed with smaller gills. Free from or only slightly attached to the stalk. Creamy in color with pink tinges; often patched with brown or red. Fragile.

STALK   Cylindrical or irregularly squat in the middle. Thick and solid. White, frequently with brown patches or brownish scales. At first it is covered with furfuraceous matter, particularly in the upper part; then it becomes slightly wrinkly or striate. Full, then worm-eaten and spongy.

MISTAKEN   For the deadly **Amanita phalloides** 7, which is distinguished, however, by a ring on the stalk, a volva around a bulbous base, and a cap surface that is somewhat moist and not split.

Russula virescens (Greenish Russula)

EDIBLE But mediocre. It requires long cooking or heavy seasoning. Nevertheless it is highly prized and sought after in some European regions and in the United States, particularly in the Western states.

HABITAT Summer until the end of autumn. In coniferous and hardwood forests, but more commonly in the latter. Solitary or gregarious. It often grows in rings.

CAP It is meatier when the gills are narrower. At first it is convex with a central depression; later it is expanded, often irregularly, and goblet- or funnel-shaped. From 2-6½ inches in diameter. At first the margin curves under toward the gills and is covered with fine down; later it slowly withdraws and becomes fully uncurled when the fungus is fully mature. Generally the cap is lobed and undulate. When the fungus is mature the margin is often cracked along the lines of the gills below. The cuticle is white, off-white, light brown, or covered with light brown patches. As the fungus emerges from the earth it breaks the crust of the soil; hence the cap is often covered with clots of dirt, twigs, and other plant detritus, sometimes with pieces of large size.

GILLS Very distant in the typical form of this fungus; more or less close in other varieties. Often branching toward the margin of the cap. Somewhat decurrent along the stalk. White or cream with blue-green tinges. In the variety **chloroides**, the gills are light blue-green. The gills of the young fungus exude tiny watery drops that are not latex and look like dew.

STALK Cylindrical, short, and squat. It often becomes narrower toward the base. White, frequently with brownish spots. It has greenish tinges near the gills. Smooth at first, later acquiring large grooves. Hard and full.

FLESH Hard, fragile, and granulose. White, but turning somewhat brownish or reddish after being exposed to the air for a few hours. The flesh of the mature fungus has a fishy odor. The taste is sharp, at least that of the gills.

MISTAKEN For the white **Lactarii**: **controversus** 79, **vellereus** 80, and **piperatus** 81, which all exude latex when ulcerated. Mistaken for **R. vesicatoria** which has a very persistent acrid taste and is distinguished from **R. delica** by a lack of the blue-green tint on gills and stalk.

Russula delica (Weaned Russula)

(Yellow Russula)

EXCELLENT   It cooks very quickly.

HABITAT   Summer and autumn. In coniferous and hardwood forests. Gregarious growing in small numbers.

CAP   Convex, turning plane and sometimes depressed. From 3/4-2 inches in diameter. The margin is thin and uncracked. As the fungus ages the margin becomes ridged parallel to the gills. The cuticle is viscid when the air is damp and is easily detached from the flesh of the cap. In color it is a warm yellow, the color of egg yolk, ochre yellow, rusty yellow or other shades of yellow.

GILLS   Close and equal. Joined by veining. Free from the stalk or only barely touching it. Thin, fragile, and white turning light brown.

STALK   Cylindrical and fairly long. White and slightly wrinkly. Soft and fragile Spongy, then hollow.

FLESH   Fragile and white. Odorless. The taste is mild.

MISTAKEN   For various other yellow **Russulae**, including the inedible **ochroleuca** 93, the poisonous **fellea**, and the inedible **pectinata**, but all these **Russulae** have a sharp taste. When in doubt, test a small piece of the mushroom on the tongue without swallowing and discard it if the taste is sharp.

Russula lutea (Yellow Russula)

INEDIBLE   Because of its sharp taste.

HABITAT   Summer and autumn. In woodlands.

CAP   Convex and sometimes gibbose; then expanded and more or less deeply depressed. From 1 1/2-4 1/2 inches in diameter. The margin is often undulate and irregular in shape. Even when the fungus has reached full maturity, the margin is slightly bent downward. At first it is smooth, but as the fungus reaches maturity, the margin becomes ridged parallel to the gills. The cuticle can be easily detached in large strips from the flesh of the cap. It is moist, bright, slightly wrinkled, and sometimes has large reddish granules. The cap is usually olive yellow but darker at the center. It may also be ochre yellow or reddish ochre, but always much darker toward the center. The variety **citrina** is lemon yellow in color.

GILLS   Sometimes close; sometimes less close. Rarely branching. Broad. The gills do not reach to the stalk or only barely. They are cream colored.

STALK   Cylindrical. The length of the stem is usually equal to the diameter of the cap, but it may be somewhat shorter. Solid and smooth. White, turning grayish or brownish and becoming covered with fine striations. Stuffed, becoming spongy.

FLESH   Tender, fragile, and thick. White but grayish when the weather is damp. It later turns brownish and develops small ochre or reddish spots. Slight odor. Sharp taste, but sometimes very mild.

MISTAKEN   For the excellent **Russula lutea** 92, which always has a mild taste.

N. B.   In the illustration on the opposite page, the specimen to the right is of the variety **citrina**.

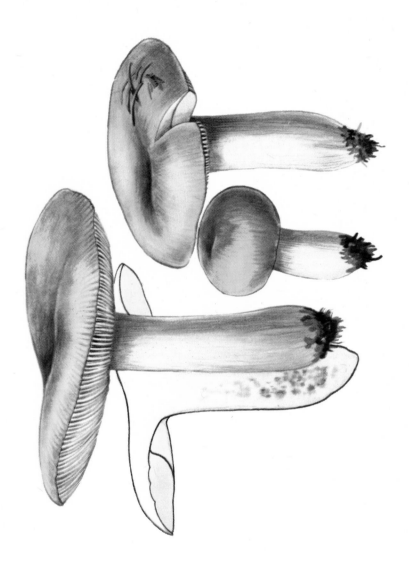

Russula ochroleuca (Ochrey Russula)

SUSPECT   Some sources consider it slightly poisonous.

HABITAT   Summer and autumn. In coniferous and hardwood forests. In damp places. Gregarious.

CAP   Hemispherical or almost globular; later convex; and finally expanded and more or less irregular in shape. It may also be concave. From 1 1/2-6 1/2 inches in diameter. The margin is grooved all over, parallel to the gills below. As the fungus matures, the margin becomes irregular in form: it becomes undulate, lobed, and cracks along the gills. The ridges become more pronounced and even knobby. The cuticle is sticky at first, particularly along the margin; then it becomes dry and is usually marked by radial striation or grooves. It is easily detached from the cap. When detached it appears diaphanous and almost colorless. The cap is ochre yellow and darker, i.e., brown, at the center. There are occasional reddish spots. As the fungus ages the color fades and becomes grayish ochre.

GILLS   Rather distant. Very thick and unequal in length. There is occasional branching. Veined. Free from or barely touching the stalk. Whitish, turning cream colored with brownish patches. The young fungus exudes dewy drops.

STALK   Cylindrical. The middle is often squatty. Rather thick. Whitish in color it soon acquires brownish patches. A bit rough to the touch. Near the gills it is covered with coarse furfuraceous matter. Rigid and solid. It soon becomes spongy with reddish clots, then hollow and very fragile.

FLESH   Hard and fragile. Whitish, it turns brownish when exposed to the air. The odor is of bitter almonds in young speciments then fetid and similar to that of burnt wool. The taste is awful.

Russula foetens (Fetid Russula)

95 RUSSULA ALBONIGRA

EDIBLE But inferior in quality.

HABITAT Summer and autumn. In coniferous and hardwood forests, especially beech.

CAP Plane or convex at first, turning plane or concave. It is sometimes funnel-shaped. From 2-4 inches in diameter. At first the margin is curled toward the gills and smooth. Later, although it remains curved down, it becomes irregularly undulate. The cuticle is slightly viscid. White, turning ashy gray. The fungus turns black at the slightest touch, particularly along the margin, the gills, and the stalk. Usually the margin is a bit lighter in color than the rest of the cap.

GILLS Close, thin, and unequal. Branching, adnexed to the stalk, and somewhat decurrent. Milk-white in color, turning light brown and finally grayish.

STALK Cylindrical and squat. Gray, then brownish or blackish. Hard and full, often becoming worm-eaten.

FLESH Hard, fragile, and white. It turns grayish at once on exposure to the air. Odorless. The taste is mild or slightly sharp.

MISTAKEN HARMLESSLY For the edible **Russula nigricans** 96, which has distant and very thick gills. Mistaken harmlessly for the edible **Russula adusta**, which is usually darker in color than the variety **albonigra**. Mistaken harmlessly for the edible **Hygrophorus camarophyllus**, which has distant and decurrent gills.

Russula albonigra (Scorched Russula)

EDIBLE But inferior in quality.

HABITAT Summer and autumn. In coniferous and hardwood forests.

CAP Hemispherical, then convex with a small pit in the center; later plane and slightly concave; and finally concave and crater-shaped. From 2½-7 inches in diameter. At first the margin curves under toward the gills; later it withdraws and becomes undulate. The cuticle is smooth and viscid, but soon becomes dry and can be detached from the cap flesh only along the margin. It is white or whitish yellow at first, then turns a smoky brown, and finally it is covered with blackish patches.

GILLS Very distant and very thick. Broad. Touching the stalk. Creamy white, turning yellowish, and later smoky or blackish.

STALK Cylindrical and squat. The base may be either broader, or narrower than the stalk. White with brownish then later blackish patches. Full and then stuffed with blackish pith.

FLESH The thickness of the flesh of the cap depends on the breadth of the gills. As the one is thicker, the other is narrower. But the flesh is always rather thick. Hard and grainy. White. The flesh of younger fungi becomes reddish on contact with the air and then blackish. The odor is mild and perhaps slightly repugnant. The taste is slightly sharp. The mature fungus can be kept for a long time without spoiling.

MISTAKEN HARMLESSLY For the edible **Russula albonigra** 95, which has close and slender gills. Mistaken harmlessly for the edible **Russula adusta,** which also has very close gills but they are much thinner than those of **Russula nigricans**; the flesh turns not red but brown then grey and only after a long time black. Mistaken harmlessly for **Hygrophorus camarophyllus**, which is edible and has distant gills that are decurrent along the stalk.

Russula nigricans (Blackish Russula)

EDIBLE One of the best edible mushrooms. Sort before cooking and discard specimens with a bitterish taste.

HABITAT Summer and autumn, until the beginning of winter. In open grassy hardwood, especially oak, forests.

CAP Convex and sometimes irregular at first; later expanded with a broad flat umbo in the center, though it may also be very depressed in the center. From 4-8 inches in diameter. The margin is thin and always remains curved under toward the gills. It is undulate, generally with small lobes; here and there are deep grooves or cracks. When the fungus is mature, there are cracks parallel to the gills. Purplish violet in color with small more darkly tinged patches. The center is covered with often very coarse furfuraceous matter, brownish violet in color. It is viscid.

GILLS Subdistant but intersected by many smaller gills. Rather narrow. Toward the stalk they grow even narrower and come to a point that touches the stalk. White to pinkish in color at first, they develop violaceous or violet red tinges. When bruised they become somewhat darker and the edge becomes violet brown here and there.

STALK Cylindrical. Sometimes it takes the shape of a goatskin bottle; sometimes the middle is drawn in, the upper part narrows toward the cap, and the base is squat. Very squat and thick. Often slightly curving. White then staining with violet or violet-red tinges like the cap. Fibrillose. The upper part is covered with violet scales or granules; the lower part is covered with white furfuraceous matter that is barely noticeable.

FLESH White with violaceous tinges. The odor is pleasant. The taste is usually bitterish and only rarely mild.

Hygrophorus russula (Russula Hygrophorus)

GOOD

HABITAT   From the end of summer till the beginning of winter. In pastures. Alon footpaths. In the grass.

CAP   Conical or campanulate, then plane with an umbo in the center, finall goblet-shaped as a rule. From 3/4-2 inches in diameter. The margin is thin, mor or less noticeably striate. The cuticle is glabrous and dry. White or pale grayis white in color. Sometimes it has cream or brown tinges in the center. The colo is brighter when the air is damp. The cap is so transparent that one can se the gills through the flesh.

GILLS   Not close. Rather broad and fairly thick. Interspersed with smaller gill The gill edge is sinuate. Somewhat decurrent along the stalk. White.

STALK   It resembles an upside-down cone. Slender. White though often pinkis at the base. Quite wrinkly or at least fibrillose. Stuffed, becoming complete hollow.

FLESH   Thin and fragile, and very pale in color. The odor is barely perceptibl The taste is pleasant.

MISTAKEN   For the poisonous **Clitocybe dealbata** 67, which has close and rela tively thin gills.

MISTAKEN HARMLESSLY   For the good **Hygrophorus chrysodon** 99, which ha golden-yellow flocculose matter on the cap margin. Mistaken harmlessly for th edible **Hygrophorus eburneus**, which does not have an umbo on the cap. Mistake harmlessly for the edible **Hygrophorus cossus**, which has a very nauseating odo

Hygrophorus niveus (Snow-white Hygrophorus)

GOOD

HABITAT   Summer and autumn. In coniferous and hardwood forests, particularly oak and beech. More common in mountainous zones.

CAP   Convex, becoming expanded with an umbo in the center or somewhat gibbose. From 2-3¼ inches in diameter. The cap margin is thin. The cuticle is very viscid. White in color, it is covered with golden-yellow flocculose matter, which is denser along the cap margin. The cap becomes spotted pale yellow at the touch. When the fungus is mature it is pale yellow in color.

GILLS   Distant and very broad. Rather thin. At first they are adnexed to the stalk, and later they are somewhat decurrent. White at first with yellow floccose edges, they later turn creamy in color.

STALK   Cylindrical and sometimes narrower at the base. Often it is very curved. White and covered, particularly in the upper portion, with flocculose matter arranged in ring fashion. These floccules are white at first and then turn bright yellow. The stalk turns pale yellow at the touch. Viscid and tender. Stuffed at first, then hollow.

FLESH   Tender, watery, and white. Odorless and almost tasteless.

MISTAKEN   For the poisonous **Clitocybe dealbata** 67, which has close gills.

MISTAKEN HARMLESSLY   For the good **Hygrophorus niveus** 98, for the edible **Hygrophorus eburneus**, and for the edible **Hygrophorus cossus**, none of which have golden flocculi on the cap.

Good

Hygrophorus chrysodon (Yellow Downy)

GOOD

HABITAT Summer and autumn. In coniferous woods. On the edge of the woods or in clearings. In mossy places. It is found more commonly in mountainous areas.

CAP Gibbose or companulate, then convex, and finally plane. From 1 1/2-2 3/4 inches in diameter. The margin is curved toward the gills at first, then it withdraws and becomes undulate. The cuticle is sticky. The center of the cap is dotted with glutinous papillae. The cuticle is smooth and glabrous. Pearly gray, brownish gray, pale violet-gray, or yellowish gray in color. The color is deeper toward the center and paler toward the margin.

GILLS Not distant. Broad and thick and interspersed with smaller gills. Occasional branching. Decurrent along the stalk. White or off-white in color.

STALK Cylindrical and slender. It is often very curved. It is usually somewhat squatty at the base. Off-white or pale brown in color. Covered with white flocculi, particularly toward the top. A bit wrinkled or fibrillose. Dry, firm, and full.

FLESH Tender and watery. White but the flesh immediately beneath the cap cuticle is gray. It has a pleasant characteristic odor of bitter almonds or anise. The taste is pleasant and bitterish.

Good

Hygrophorus agathosmus

EXCELLENT

HABITAT   From March, even under the snow, till May. There is also a variety that grows in the autumn. In coniferous woods or beech forests. Often hidden under fallen leaves. Gregarious.

CAP   Globose, then plane or even depressed and slightly gibbose. From 1½-4 inches in diameter. The margin at first curves under toward the gills. Later it expands and becomes undulate and sometimes irregularly rippled. The cuticle may be very viscid but it quickly dries. It is smooth and glabrous. Pearl-gray with blackish spots at first, it turns darker, albeit lighter at the center; in the end it becomes blackish all over.

GILLS   Close, narrow, and very thick at first. Later very distant and rather thin. Occasional branching. Interspersed with smaller gills. Veined. Very decurrent along the stalk. White turning grayish with lighter edges; sometimes they become blackish.

STALK   Cylindrical, short and squatty. Often curved. White, turning silvery gray from the bottom up. The upper part is covered with fine furfuraceous matter that comes away easily. Dry, silky, fibrillose, and stuffed.

FLESH   Tender and somewhat fibrous. Whitish with gray marbling. The flesh is grayish under the cap cuticle and toward the cap margin. In the end the flesh is all gray. The odor and taste are mild.

Hygrophorus marzuolus

GOOD Tender. Rarely bothered by insects. It loses all its qualities if it is frozen.

HABITAT Summer and autumn; particularly in the month of September. It can be found in the plains, but it is more common in mountainous areas. On the edge of woods and along roads. In places where vegetation is scanty, where it is moist and grassy. Gregarious. Scattered in groups or tufts.

CAP Campanulate, then plane but gibbose. It may have an umbo in the center. From 1½-3¼ inches in diameter. The margin is thin. The cuticle is smooth, glabrous, dry, and often cracked. Pale orange, reddish or bread-crust colored.

GILLS Not close. Rather broad. Veined. Very decurrent along the stalk. White turning pinkish ochre. It may be a paler tint of the color of the cap.

STALK Cylindrical and usually curving. Short. The base is often pointed. The lower part is striate or fibrillose. White at first, turning a paler tint of the cap color. Stuffed but often becoming hollow.

FLESH Firm and fragile. Whitish, turning ochre yellow. Almost odorless. The taste is pleasant.

MISTAKEN HARMLESSLY For **Hygrophorus nemorensis**, an edible fungus that is slenderer, slightly striate on the cap, and is covered with fine furfuraceous matter on the lower part of the stalk.

Hygrophorus (Camarophyllus) pratensis
(Meadow Hygrophorus)

103 HYGROPHORUS PUNICEUS
HYGROCYBE PUNICEA

(Red Hygrophorus)

GOOD   It tastes like chicken.

HABITAT   Later summer and autumn. In hilly and mountainous regions. In damp or mossy places; in grassy fields and woods. Gregarious.

CAP   Conical or campanulate, becoming convex or plane; it almost always has a broad umbo in the center. From 2½-5 inches in diameter. The margin is often somewhat undulate and soon becomes lobed. Then it splits here and there along the lines of the gills below. The cuticle is viscid at first. It is glabrous and sometimes has radial fibrils. As the fungus matures the cap color fades: from scarlet to orange yellow. The color appears paler, too, when the air is dry, and the cuticle is dry.

GILLS   Not close. Interspersed with smaller gills. Very broad and thick. At first adnexed to the stalk, but as the fungus matures they become free from it. Fragile. Yellowish at first, turning reddish. The gill edge remains yellow. Covered with fine powder when the fungus is mature.

STALK   Cylindrical and quite thick. Sometimes curved. Yellow or orange-yellow with red areas. Slightly reticulate near the gills. Grooved by fibrils. Purplish around the middle; whitish and cottony at the base. Fragile and empty. The stalk cavity is yellow.

FLESH   Very firm. The color is that of the stalk or paler. The flesh just beneath the cap cuticle is orange. The odor is insignificant. The taste is insipid.

MISTAKEN HARMLESSLY   For various related species which are edible or at least innocuous.

Hygrophorus puniceus (Red Hygrophorus)
Hygrocybe punicea

GOOD WITH CAUTION It is best when fried. This mushroom is reported as producing mild poisoning in some people. Take the precautions outlined in the section **WARNING**.

HABITAT Summer and autumn. In woodlands, especially coniferous. On stumps but also on the ground.

CAP Convex or compressed, becoming plane or convex and sometimes concave in the form of a goblet. From 3/4-3 inches in diameter. The margin is thin and curved under toward the gills; later it withdraws and becomes undulate. The color changes according to the variety: orange-yellow, brownish yellow, or even, though rarely, off-white. It is generally lighter along the margin. Dry, velvety, and silky.

GILLS Close and thin. Quite narrow. Repeatedly forked. The edge is obtuse. Decurrent along the stalk. At first the gills are the color of the cap; later they become lighter.

STALK Cylindrical and often squatty at the base. Generally slender, but occasionally quite squat. Curved. The color of the cap or even a bit darker. It is generally darker at the base. Elastic. Stuffed, then hollow. There is a clear hollow in the base but this diminishes farther up toward the cap.

FLESH Flabby, almost spongy. The basic color is that of the cap, but much paler. The flesh of the stalk is even paler. The odor is almost imperceptible. The taste is very unpleasant.

MISTAKEN For the poisonous **Clitocybe olearia** 64, which is distinguished, however, by the fact that it grows in clusters.

MISTAKEN HARMLESSLY For the good **Cantharellus cibarius** (Chanterelle) 153, which has a full stalk and does not have genuine gills but more or less prominent nervature.

Hygrophoropsis aurantiaca (False Chanterelle)

INEDIBLE   When raw.

EDIBLE   Only as long as the margin is still curved under toward the gills. Then it becomes flaccid. It should be handled carefully to preserve its appearance, because the gills turn brown at the touch. Since the taste is acidulous it should be used in small quantities and mixed with fungi of other species. It can be dried.

HABITAT   Summer and autumn. In hardwood and coniferous forests. On plant detritus, dead roots, and old stumps. In damp sheltered places, along pits and footpaths, fields.

CAP   Convex with the margin curled in the form of an Ionic volute toward the gills; later plane; then depressed and sometimes curved in like a bowl. When the cap expands it becames irregular in shape. From 2-6 inches in diameter. A bit viscid when the air is damp; shiny when the air is dry. Velvety, particularly along the margin. Ochre, cinnamon brown, or olive brown in color; it yellows as the fungus ages. Sometimes it is covered with broad darker scales.

GILLS   Very close and branching. Not broad. Toward the stalk the gills are joined by veining and look pitted, as a honey-comb. Decurrent along the stalk. Pale cream at first, turning ochre yellow. When rubbed they turn brownish red and stain the fingers. Very fragile; a flick of the nail can remove them from the cap. They can be removed in clumps from the cap.

STALK   Cylindrical and often somewhat squat at the base and narrowing toward the cap. Short and curved. It is occasionally off-center to the cap. When the fungus is picked, cottony filamentous pieces with detritus remain attached to the base. The same color as the cap. Smooth and glabrous or somewhat fibrillose. Solid, firm, and full.

FLESH   Tender, becoming flaccid. Juicy. Yellowish but turning reddish brown when exposed to the air. Crushed it turns reddish. The odor is acidulous and fruity. The taste is acidulous and pleasant.

MISTAKEN   For various **Lactarii**, but the **Lactarii** exude latex as soon as they are touched.

Paxillus involutus (Involute Paxillus)

GOOD Summer and late autumn. In coniferous woods, especially pine, but also in hardwood forests. Solitary or scattered.

CAP Conical, campanulate, or hemispherical; later convex, usually with a slight umbo in the center. From 1½ to 4 inches in diameter. The margin curves under toward the gills. In the young fungus the margin is joined to the stalk by a kind of veil. Glabrous, smooth. Viscid when the air is damp. Coppery brown with wine-red tinges. Occasionally it is yellowish brown or reddish, but usually only when very mature.

GILLS Not close. Branching. Very broad and very thick. Decurrent along the stalk. Yellowish gray, turning violaceous gray. The gill edge is flocculose and somewhat lighter in color. The gills are easily detached from the cap.

STALK Cylindrical, narrowing toward the base; or in the form of an inverted truncated cone. Generally long and somewhat curved. The color is that of the cap, except toward the base, which may be saffron yellow. There are encircling scaly zones and a pseudo-annulus, the remains of the veil, but these tend to disappear. Somewhat viscid. Fibrillose, firm, and full.

VEIL In the immature fungus, the cap margin is connected to the stalk by a veil that may be filamentous or soft depending on whether the air is dry or damp. The color of the veil is lighter than that of the cap. As the fungus matures this veil withdraws around the stalk and forms a kind of ring, more or less entire, that is brownish in color and survives even in the mature fungus.

FLESH Solid. Pinkish yellow. The flesh of the stalk base is saffron yellow. The flesh turns somewhat pink when exposed to the air. The odor is mild and the taste is pleasant.

Gomphidius rutilus (Viscid Gomphidius)

GOOD It can be dried.

HABITAT Summer and autumn. In coniferous woods, especially fir. Chiefly in mountainous regions. It may be gregarious.

CAP Convex, then plane, and finally depressed. Rarely it may have a slightly pronounced umbo in the center. From 1 1/2-5 1/2 inches in diameter. The margin is thin. At first it curves under toward the gills; then it slowly unwinds. The surface is smooth and glabrous. There is a glutinous layer on the surface that can easily be separated. When the fungus is dried, this glutin takes on the appearance of a crust of shiny wax. Violaceous gray, violaceous brown, or chestnut in color. As the fungus ages, the surface often becomes marked with tiny spots or stripes that are black and look like ink.

GILLS Not close. Very broad. Thick. The edge is serrate. Branching. Interspersed with some smaller gills. Veined. Decurrent along the stalk. White turning gray and finally blackish.

STALK Cylindrical. Sometimes squat, sometimes slender. Occasionally curved at the base. Whitish above the brown remains of the veil; all the rest is bright yellow with violet-gray or black patches, particularly at the base; later it turns blackish. Covered with the same glutinous matter that covers the cap. Stuffed.

VEIL In the immature fungus the cap margin is joined to the stalk by a veil that is filamentous or soft depending on whether the air is damp or dry. Ashy or violet-white in color. As the fungus matures this veil withdraws around the stalk and forms a kind of ring, more or less total. Brownish in color, it survives even in the mature fungus.

FLESH Tender, fragile, and white. The flesh under the cap cuticle, however, is slightly brownish. The flesh of the lower half of the stalk is bright lemon yellow in color. The odor is slight. The taste is acidulous.

Gomphidius glutinosus (Glutinous Gomphidius)

NOT RECOMMENDED Inferior, hard, and unattractive.

HABITAT Summer and autumn. Chiefly in hardwood forests. Less common in mountainous regions.

CAP Almost spherical, then convex, and finally resembling a round pincushion. From 2-6 inches in diameter. The margin ends in a noticeable and uneven flocculose fringe. At first it is white and covered with large gray granules; then it turns grayish and cracks, becoming covered with large polygonal scales that are dry, floccose, blackish brown, and arranged like tiles.

PORES Large and polygonal. Whitish, turning grayish and then blackish. They turn reddish at the touch.

TUBES Long but becoming shorter near the stalk, to which they are attached. Whitish, turning reddish or grayish when wounded, then dark brown or black.

STALK Cylindrical. Sometimes long and thin; sometimes long and thick; sometimes no longer than the cap diameter. Usually squat at the base and narrowing toward the cap. Occasionally a bit curved. Whitish and smooth from the ring up; from the ring down, it is blackish gray and covered with darker floccose tufts that are quite thick. Hard, stuffed, and fibrous.

RING Floccose and grayish. It tends to fall off, and mature specimens often lack the ring.

FLESH Hard, tough. The flesh of the stem is leathery. White but turning grayish and blackish as the fungus ages. When exposed to the air, the flesh turns reddish, orange, or pink, then violet gray, and finally blackish. The odor is almost imperceptible. The taste is mild.

Strobilomyces floccopus (Pine Cone Mushroom)

109 BOLETUS AURANTIACUS
LECCINUM AURANTIACUM

GOOD But it does not keep long. Once picked, it should be cooked as soon as possible. It turns blackish in cooking. It is fine for preparing mushroom extract.

HABITAT Summer and autumn. In hardwood forests, under poplars and willows. Less common in coniferous woods.

CAP Hemispherical, then convex, and quite late assuming the form of a round pincushion. From 1 1/2-5 1/2 inches in diameter. The margin remains curved under toward the tubes. Much later it withdraws and then the cap cuticle, which has become membranous, extends beyond the edge of the margin here and there. Orange, reddish orange, or brownish orange in color. In the variety **rufescens** the cuticle is velvety and orange-yellow in color.

PORES Close, small, and round. Off-white or cream colored, soon turning grayish.

TUBES Long and thin. Either detached from the stalk or barely adnexed. Soft. Whitish or cream colored.

STALK Cylindrical or truncated cone in form. The length is equal to twice the diameter of the cap. Grayish or brownish gray. As the fungus matures, the stalk becomes covered with raised flocculi, white at first but turning brownish red. They are blackish in the variety **rufescens**. These flocculi, which appear more densely on the upper part of the stalk are arranged longitudinally.

FLESH That of the cap is a bit soft, while that of the stem is hard. White, turning pink or violet and then blackish gray. That of the base is light blue. The odor is pleasant as is the taste.

MISTAKEN HARMLESSLY For the good **Boletus leucophaseus**, the flesh of which, however, does not turn black. Mistaken harmlessly for **Boletus (Leccinum) durius-culus**, a good fungus that is darker and squatter than **Boletus (Leccinum) auran-tiacus**. Mistaken harmlessly for **Boletus (Leccinum) scaber** 110, a good fungus that is not orange in color.

Boletus auricantiacus (Orange-cap Boletus)
Leccinum aurantiacum

GOOD It must be eaten soon after it is gathered because it does not keep well. It can be used to make mushroom extract.

HABITAT Summer and autumn. In hardwood forests, particularly under spruce, birch, and hazel.

CAP Hemispherical, then convex and campanulate, and finally expanded into the shape of a pincushion. When the fungus is fully mature there may be occasional small depressions that resemble thumbprints in soft dough. From 1½-5½ inches in diameter. The margin remains curved under toward the tubes for some time; then it withdraws and the cuticle of the cap, which has become membranous, extends beyond the margin at some points. The surface is ashy gray, brownish gray, or blackish ochre; sometimes it is simply blackish; sometimes it is a pale ashy color or, in another variety, off-white. Viscid when the air is damp.

PORES Very small. Round. Yellowish white turning grayish.

TUBES Thin and long, rounded toward the stalk, which they barely touch or do not touch at all. Off-white, turning grayish. Soft.

STALK Cylindrical or in the form of an elongated truncated cone. Sometimes slightly curved or twisted. Grayish white and covered with stiff protruding scales. White or yellowish at first, then blackish; arranged longitudinally. Hard and stuffed.

FLESH Soft. White but rapidly turning pink, reddish and slightly violet when exposed to the air; later it turns grayish then finally blackish. Even when dried or cooked the flesh turns blackish. It does not keep well. The odor and taste are pleasant.

MISTAKEN HARMLESSLY For the good **Boletus (Leccinum) aurantiacus** 109, which is basically orange, however. Mistaken hamlessly for the good **Boletus leucophaseus**, the flesh of which does not turn black. Mistaken for the good **Boletus (Leccinum) duriusculus**, which grows under poplars or - in the variety **griseus** - under birch, and which is squatter and darker than **Boletus (Leccinum) scaber**.

Boletus scaber (Rough-stemmed Boletus)
Leccinum scabrum

111 BOLETUS EDULIS   (Cep; Edible Boletus; King Boletus; Steinpilz)

EXCELLENT Even raw in salad. It can be dried. It can also be kept under oil.

HABITAT Summer and autumn. In coniferous and hardwood forests. Particularly in open places and on the edge of woodlands.

CAP Hemispherical, then convex, and finally pincushion-shaped, occasionally depressed and usually very irregular in form. From 2-8 inches in diameter, but sometimes much larger. At first the margin is curved under toward the tubes; later it withdraws and is sometimes very uneven. The basic surface color is brown: hazel, chestnut, purplish brown, yellowish or grayish brown, but it may also be off-white. Usually the margin is paler in color. Depending on the variety, the surface may be slightly rough or velvety. A bit viscid when the air is damp.

PORES Small, roundish, and regular. Off-white, turning yellowish and then greenish yellow.

TUBES Long and thin. Toward the stalk they become round and are free of it or barely touching. White or off-white, turning yellowish and finally greenish yellow. Easily detached from the cap.

STALK Ovoid, then pear-shaped; as the fungus matures the stalk tends to become cylindrical, but it sometimes takes on other shapes. It is always thick and solid. White or light hazel in color, and lighter toward the base. Covered more or less extensively by a network that is tight and long and starts at the top, lighter than the rest of the stem at first, then turning darker. This reticulation is often quite faint. The stem is hard, stuffed, later becoming spongy and fibrous.

FLESH Firm, but soft in mature specimens. White in color. The flesh immediately under the cap cuticle, however, is vinaceous or brownish in color. The flesh immediately around the tubes is white, but in the variety **reticulatus** it is yellow. It does not change color on contact with the air. The odor and taste are pleasant.

MISTAKEN For the inedible **Boletus (Tylopilus) felleus** 112, which has white pores that turn pink, very prominent reticulation on the stem and a bitter taste.

Boletus edulis (Cep)

112 BOLETUS FELLEUS
TYLOPILUS FELLEUS

INEDIBLE Extremely bitter, though not poisonous. It only takes one to render impalatable all the other fungi with which it has been mistakenly cooked.

HABITAT Summer and autumn. In hard or mixed woods. Particularly on sandy ground.

CAP Hemispherical, then convex, then pincushion-shaped, and sometimes plane or depressed, with the margin turned up. From 2-5 inches in diameter. The margin is often lobed and undulate. The cuticle is dry, velvety, and not easily detached from the flesh of the cap. Crust brown, hazel- or honey-colored.

PORES Very small. Round becoming angular. White turning pink.

TUBES Long. Adnexed and decurrent along the stem, or totally free. White or cream-colored, then flesh pink when mature.

STALK Pear-shaped, but in the fully mature fungus it may be cylindrical, albeit irregularly. A bit lighter in color than the cap. Reticulate and noticeably so on the upper part of the stalk. The reticulation is brownish. Stuffed.

FLESH Very soft. White, but brown under the cuticle of the cap. Rarely it has occasional light blue patches. It turns pink on contact with the air. The odor is faint, and the taste is bitter.

MISTAKEN When young for the excellent **Boletus edulis** 111, and for the excellent **Boletus aereus**, which do not have raised reticulation or bitter taste.

Boletus (Tylopilus) felleus (Bitter Boletus)

113 BOLETUS CASTANEUS
GYROPORUS CASTANEUS

GOOD

HABITAT   Summer and autumn. In gravelly and grassy woodlands. Solitary or gregarious.

CAP   Convex at first, then plane or plane-depressed and gibbose. From 2-4 inches in diameter. The thin margin is undulate. The surface is covered with velvety down. It varies in color from cinnamon to chestnut brown.

PORES   Small, round and white, turning pale lemon yellow.

TUBES   Short. The tubes nearest the stem are very short and somewhat decurrent. White becoming creamy yellow.

STALK   Cylindrical with a squat base. Rather thick. Finely grooved longitudinally. Completely covered with down. Stuffed but later with large hollow spaces.

FLESH   That of the cap is hard and fragile; that of the stalk is spongy. White. The odor is mild. It has a hazelnut taste.

Boletus (Gyroporus) castaneus (Chestnut Boletus)

EXCELLENT Raw or cooked. It can also be dried or kept in oil.

HABITAT Summer and autumn. In woodlands.

CAP Hemispherical, then assuming the form of a round pincushion. From 2½-8 inches in diameter. Not viscid but dry. Velvety. Sepia or blackish brown, it sometimes has lighter patches.

PORES Small and roundish. White at first covered with a delicate moist powdery substance; then greenish yellow.

TUBES Thin and rather long. The length increases as the fungus matures. They become rounded toward the stalk. They adhere only to the top of the stalk. White turning yellowish and finally olive.

STALK Globose at first or ovoid, then pear-shaped or cylindrical. Usually squat at the base. Solid. Light pinkish hazel. Closely reticulate, the webbing is brown in color. Rarely this reticulation may be totally absent.

FLESH Firm and white. The odor and taste are pleasant.

MISTAKEN When still young for the inedible **Boletus felleus** 112, which has a distinct raised reticulation on the stem and a bitter taste.

Boletus aereus

115 BOLETUS SATANAS (Satan's Boletus)

POISONOUS This is the only one of the tube-bearing fungi that is genuinely poisonous when raw. It causes violent vomiting. Some people can eat it cooked, however, without suffering any ill effects, while others develop gastro-enteritis.

HABITAT Summer. In hardwood forests, especially beech. Along the edge of woods and in open places. It grows in the grass.

CAP Hemispherical and together with the stalk resembling a ball or egg at first; then convex, and finally pincushion-shaped. From 2-12 inches in diameter. The margin is somewhat undulate and occasionally rough-edged. The surface color is whitish gray or leaden gray, but it later turns very yellow or olive and becomes marked with yellow, pink, greenish, and grayish patches. At first it is finely velvety, but it becomes glabrous and dry after a while.

PORES Small and roundish or slightly irregular. Yellow, turning blood red, then orange red, and finally brownish. As the fungus ages and when bruised, the pores turn bluish green in color.

TUBES Short at first, becoming quite long. Rounded toward the stalk, which they touch only barely or not at all. Yellow, turning greenish. They turn light blue at the touch.

STALK Oval at first, then pear-shaped. Short and squat. Yellow above, red about the middle, and yellowish or brownish toward the base. It has red patches. The blood-red polygonal reticulation may turn pink, white, or olive here and there. The reticulation is usually darker in color than the rest of the stalk. Sometimes there is no reticulation, in which case the stalk is covered with red or olive patches. When the fungus is picked these colors quickly disappear. In the young fungus, the stalk is velvety. It turns bluish at the touch. Hard and full.

FLESH Solid, becoming somewhat spongy. Whitish, occasionally with yellow zones. It becomes slightly bluish on contact with the air, but this color quickly vanishes. The odor is sweet in young specimens but characteristic and disagreeable when mature. The taste is mild.

MISTAKEN For **Boletus albidus** 116, which is inedible because of its bitter taste. Mistaken for the suspect **Boletus purpureus**, which has a yellowish cap suffused with pink.

Boletus Satanas (Satan's Boletus)

INEDIBLE It is not toxic but the taste is bitter.

HABITAT Summer and autumn. In hardwood forests. On the edge of woods, in dry places, and in moss.

CAP Hemispherical, then convex, and finally expanded in the shape of a round pincushion; somewhat gibbose. From 4-8 inches in diameter. The margin is curved under toward the tubes at first but later withdraws. The cuticle is dry and sometimes split. Whitish, ashy, hazel, or olive in color, but always a pale tint.

PORES Thin and round. Pale lemon yellow in color. They turn bluish green at the touch.

TUBES Very long. Thin. Almost free from the stalk. Lemon yellow in color with greenish tinges.

STALK Ovoid, then lengthening. It becomes knotty and wrinkled. Thick and robust. Off-white, grayish, or pale yellowish in color. The upper part is lemon yellow and reticulate. The base is greenish, with no trace of red.

FLESH Thick, compact, and firm. Cream-colored. The base of the stalk is olive. The flesh under the tubes is yellowish and turns bluish green, as does the flesh next to the tubes. The odor is pleasant. The taste is mild at first but turns bitter.

Boletus albidus

117 BOLETUS CYANESCENS GYROPORUS CYANESCENS

(Indigo Boletus)

EXCELLENT

HABITAT Summer and autumn. In coniferous and hardwood forests. Particularly under pine, oak, and chestnut. On sandy ground.

CAP Hemispherical at first, then plane and usually gibbose and uneven. From 2½-5 inches in diameter. The margin is curled under toward the tubes at first; later it withdraws and becomes undulate. The cuticle is dry. The color varies from milk-white to olive-yellow.

PORES Small and roundish. White, turning yellowish. They turn blue immediately on touch.

TUBES Moderately long. They barely reach the stalk. White, they turn bright blue as soon as they are touched.

STALK Cylindrical and swelling half-way up. Hard but fragile. White and smooth above; scaly and sometimes the same color as the cap from the mid-point down. Stuffed, then spongy, and finally with hollow sections.

FLESH Firm. White but turning deep blue as soon as it is cut or broken. The odor and taste are mild and pleasant.

Boletus (Gyroporus) cyanescens (Indigo Boletus)

118 BOLETUS EDULIS
subsp. PINICOLA

EXCELLENT   The cooking water turns olive in color. This bolete can be dried.

HABITAT   First in May and then again in autumn. In the mountains. In coniferous woods, especially under pine, but also in hardwood forests.

CAP   Hemispherical, then taking the shape of a round pincushion. The form is often irregular. From 4-12 inches in diameter. Velvety and slightly viscid. Along the margin it is veiled with persistent silvery down. The color ranges from reddish brown to pomegranate brown. The margin easily becomes spotted with green.

PORES   Small, roundish, and regular. White, turning yellow and finally olive.

TUBES   Thin and long. They become shorter toward the stalk, which they do not touch or only slightly. White, turning yellow and finally olive.

STALK   Oval, then pear-shaped or irregular. Thick and hard. Light brown and reticulate. The reticulation is whitish on the part of the stalk nearest the cap. The rest is brown against a slightly darker background.

FLESH   Soft, delicate, and white. The flesh immediately under the cap cuticle is light wine-red. The odor is aromatic, and the taste is pleasant.

MISTAKEN   When young, for **Boletus (Tylopilus) felleus** 112, which is inedible because of its very bitter taste.

Boletus edulis subsp. pinicola

INEDIBLE   The taste is bitter even when cooked.

HABITAT   Summer and autumn. Especially in coniferous woods, but also in hardwood forests, particularly under chestnut and oak.

CAP   Hemispherical, then convex, and finally pincushion-shaped and gibbose. From 1½-4 inches in diameter. The margin curves under toward the tubes at first, then it withdraws and becomes very uneven. The cuticle is dry. Velvety at first, it becomes glabrous. Light hazel gray, light olive gray, or light olive brown in color.

PORES   Small and roundish. Lemon-yellow, turning pale yellow. They turn light blue at the touch.

TUBES   Thin and very long. Adnexed to the stalk. Lemon yellow at first, then paler yellow, and finally olive. They turn light blue at the touch.

STALK   Cylindrical in the shape of a goatskin bottle or with a bulbous base. Rather long. Yellow above with white reticulation; purplish red throughout the rest of its length with fine reddish-pink reticulation. The base is brownish, particularly when the fungus is mature. It turns light blue at the touch. Solid and stuffed.

FLESH   Whitish or pale yellow, but that of the stalk is somewhat brownish or purplish. It turns bluish on contact with the air. The odor is characteristic. The taste is pleasant at first but then turns bitter.

MISTAKEN   For the good **Boletus luridus** 120, which has reddish flesh around the tubes and is not bitter in taste.

Boletus calopus (Scarlet-stemmed Boletus)

INEDIBLE   When raw it is not good to eat.

GOOD   When well cooked. In cooking it turns yellow. Some people can eat this mushroom; others develop gastro-enteritus. Observe cautions outlined in **WARNING**.

HABITAT   Summer and autumn. In mountainous regions and in plains. In coniferous and hardwood forests. On the edge of woods, along footpaths, and along the edge of fields.

CAP   Hemispherical, then convex, and finally round and cushion-shaped, sometimes very irregular in form. From 2-7 inches in diameter. The margin is curved under toward the tubes at first; then it withdraws and often becomes extremely undulate. At first it is delicate and velvety, and later it is covered with fine furfuraceous matter. Dry, but turning quite viscid when the air is damp. Smooth. The color varies, depending on the atmospheric conditions and the age of the fungus. It is brownish yellow at first or olive brown; then it turns a smoky brown color. The margin is often reddish. The color darkens at the touch.

PORES   Small and roundish; very irregular. Orange red or dark red in color, but golden yellow near the cap margin. The pores turn bright blue when touched.

TUBES   Thin and rather long. Shorter near the stem, from which they are free. Yellow, turning olive yellow. They turn blue at the touch.

STEM   Cylindrical or squat, sometimes misshapen. Large and solid. Yellow near the tubes, where it is also covered with small flocculi; yellowish and patched with red in the middle; purplish brown or olive brown to black at the base. Covered with broad reticulation, blood-red in color and deeper than the basic color of the stem. The reticulation is delicate and sometimes barely noticeable. Sometimes the reticulation amounts to nothing more than a dappling of red spots. It turns blue at the touch. Hard and stuffed.

FLESH   Solid. Lemon yellow or pale yellow. Reddish on the surface of the tubes; that of the base is reddish or yellow. When exposed to the air the flesh quickly turns Prussian blue in color, then green. After a while it turns purplish red. The flesh is also purplish red where the fungus has been damaged by insects. The odor is mild. The taste is pleasant.

MISTAKEN   For **Boletus calopus** 119, which is inedible; though its flesh is pleasant in taste at first, it soon turns bitter. Mistaken for **Boletus Satanas** 115, which is poisonous. The flesh of **Boletus Satanas** does not turn Prussian blue but rather only moderately light blue when cut.

MISTAKEN HARMLESSLY   For **Boletus erythropus**, which is edible when cooked. The tube surface of **erythropus** is yellow rather than red.

Good with caution

Boletus luridus (Lurid Boletus)

121 BOLETUS PULVERULENTUS

GOOD Notwithstanding its sometimes unappealing appearance.

HABITAT Summer and autumn. In mountain and plain. In fir woods. In damp and mossy sheltered places.

CAP Hemispherical at first; then round and pincushion-shaped and very gibbose. From 2¼-4¾ inches in diameter. The margin curves under toward the tubes at first; then it withdraws and becomes very undulate. When the air is damp, the surface is sticky; when the air is dry, the surface of the young fungus appears finely velveted. Later the surface is glabrous. Reddish brown in color. It turns light blue at the slightest touch, but the final color is olive.

PORES Moderate in size. From 1/2-1 millimeter. Often somewhat irregular. Golden or lemon yellow. At the slightest touch the pores turn bright blue at once, then reddish or blackish, and finally greenish yellow.

TUBES Long and rather adherent to the stalk. Easily detached from the cap. Olive in color. They instantly turn green or blue when touched.

STALK Cylindrical. The base is root-shaped and decurrent on the ground. Often curved and quite irregular in shape. Golden yellow, turning ochre-yellow or reddish brown. The middle of the stalk is dappled purplish red or reddish-purplish black; it turns blackish immediately on touch. The base turns purplish black or olive brown in the end. Solid and full.

FLESH Pale yellow, turning bright blue as soon as it is cut or broken; then it turns greenish gray. The odor is faint. The taste is pleasant in younger specimens but bitter in older ones.

Good

Boletus pulverulentus

BOLETUS BOVINUS (Shallow-pored Boletus; Cow Boletus)
SUILLUS BOVINUS

EDIBLE But very slimy. It is not fit for drying. The mature fungus is almost always full of worms.

HABITAT Summer and autumn. In mountainous regions. In larch and pinewoods. On sandy ground. In rings. It is sought after by grazing herds.

CAP Hemispherical, then convex, and finally expanded into the form of a round pincushion; very irregular in shape. From 2-4 inches in diameter. The margin is somewhat undulate. The cuticle is viscid when the air is damp, but dry and cartilaginous when the air is dry. Glabrous. As the fungus matures, the cuticle cracks and splits. Hazel or reddish brown in color.

PORES They are very large (2 millimeters) when the fungus is mature. Sharp-angled. Dentellate. On the stalk the last pores are joined and separated from each other only by small narrow decurrent gills. Olive yellow in color, turning olive brown; they become patched with brown at the touch.

TUBES Rather short. Arranged radially with a certain uniformity. Somewhat decurrent along the stalk. Grayish, turning yellowish and finally brownish.

STALK Cylindrical and narrowing toward the cap. Slender. Often curved. The color is that of the cap, but paler toward the base, where it is often enveloped by a cottony substance. Smooth and covered with fine furfuraceous matter. Fibrillose or striate. Solid, fragile, full, and fibrous.

FLESH Tender and elastic, turning soft. Yellowish. When exposed to the air some of the flesh turns slightly pinkish brown and some turns a faint blue. The odor is mild, as is the taste.

Boletus (Suillus) bovinus (Shallow-pored Boletus)

123 BOLETUS CAVIPES
BOLETINUS CAVIPES

EDIBLE Quite good as long as the fungus is not too mature; then of slight quality. It can be dried.

HABITAT Summer and autumn. In mountainous areas. In coniferous woods. Under larch. In open places and along footpaths. Sphagnum bogs.

CAP Onion-shaped at first with a clear umbo in the center; then it becomes convex and the umbo is still clearly defined; finally it expands and sometimes becomes quite sunken. From 2¼-4½ inches in diameter. In the young fungus there are often mealy, viscid, white remains of the veil hanging from the cap margin; the remainder of the veil forms the ring. In the mature fungus the margin is undulate, often lobed, and occasionally turned up. The cuticle is entirely covered with dense felty down and feels like suede to the touch. The basic color is brown but may be golden yellow, dark or light hazel, or violaceous brown.

PORES Large: 2 millimeters. Angular. Arranged in arcs that extend from the stem toward the cap margin. Pale yellow at first, turning olive yellow.

TUBES Short and decurrent along the stalk. Pale yellow at first, turning a light greenish yellow. Not easily detached from the cap.

STALK Usually rather swollen at the midpoint and resembling a goatskin bottle in shape. Often curved. Reticulate above the ring; wooly and scaly below the ring. A bit lighter in color than the cap. It is very fragile. Hollow from the beginning. After rainfall the center of the stalk is full of water.

RING White, doughy, viscid, and cobwebby at first; then cottony and yellowish.

FLESH Fairly firm. Pale or lemon yellow in color. It does not change color on exposure to the air. Odorless. The taste is mild and pleasant.

Boletus (Boletinus) cavipes (Hollow-stemmed Boletinus)

124 BOLETUS VARIEGATUS
SUILLUS VARIEGATUS

EDIBLE But inferior.

HABITAT Summer and autumn. In woodlands. Under pines. On sandy ground.

CAP Hemispherical, then convex, and finally expanded and often irregular in shape. From 2-5 inches in diameter. The thin margin curves under toward the tubes; later it expands, remains thin, and becomes very undulate. The cuticle is moist and not easily detached from the cap. It is rough but unbroken at first; later it becomes smooth but broken up into small scales which are darker than the basic color of the cap. Ochre, grayish yellow, or pale yellow.

PORES Small or medium in size. Round and angular. Close. Grayish yellow, turning olive brown. They turn light blue at the touch.

STALK Cylindrical; often squat at the base. The color is somewhat paler than that of the cap. The base is reddish brown. The stalk is partially covered with whitish felty matter. Smooth, solid, and full.

FLESH Firm, then tender and watery. Yellowish or pale orange; pale brown; reddish brown at the base. It turns faintly blue on exposure to the air. The odor is disagreeably strong; sometimes there is a faint odor of vinegar. The taste is pleasant.

Boletus (Suillus) variegatus (Variegated Boletus)

125 BOLETUS SUBTOMENTOSUS
XEROCOMUS SUBTOMENTOSUS

GOOD   In some regions it is highly prized and justly so.

HABITAT   Summer and autumn. In mountainous regions and in the plains. In coniferous and hardwood forests. In grassy places. Solitary.

CAP   Hemispherical or very convex; then expanded in the form of a round pincushion. From 1½-5 inches in diameter. The margin is very undulate. The cuticle is dry and covered with a kind of wooly felt-like matter, olive brown in color. This wooly matter later disappears and the olive-yellow color of the cap appears. As the fungus matures, the cap cracks, particularly at the center; the interior of the cracks is yellow.

PORES   Very large and unequal in size. Angular and dentellate. Bright golden yellow. They turn faintly blue at times when touched, but more often they do not change color.

TUBES   Of moderate length. They grow shorter nearer to the stalk, to which they are attached by teeth; later they appear decurrent along the stalk. Sulphurous yellow, turning olive yellow.

STALK   Cylindrical. Often narrowing toward the base and becoming slenderer toward the cap. Frequently irregular in shape. Quite curved. Yellowish with brownish zone or else reddish. At first it is covered with fine felty matter and later becomes scaly. Covered with coarse reticulation of large joined veins, darker in color than the stalk itself. Sometimes the stalk is only marked by rough longitudinal grooves.

FLESH   Firm. The flesh of the cap is whitish, that of the stalk yellowish. Under the cuticle the flesh may be slightly brown. It does not change color on exposure to the air or, if it does, it turns only slightly blue. The odor and taste are mild.

Boletus (Xerocomus) subtomentosus (Yellow-cracked Boletus)

126 BOLETUS BADIUS
XEROCOMUS BADIUS

EXCELLENT

HABITAT Summer and autumn. In coniferous woods especially under pine and in hardwood forests, especially under chestnut, oak, and beech.

CAP Hemispherical, then irregularly convex. From 1 1/2-5 1/2 inches in diameter. The thin margin is curved under toward the tubes, then withdrawn and sinuous and finally it may even be upturned. The cuticle is viscid only after the rain; when the air is dry, it is velvety. As the fungus matures the cuticle becomes smooth and shiny. It is not easily detached from the cap. Chocolate brown or dark chestnut in color.

PORES Very small and angular. Whitish, turning pale yellow and then greenish yellow. They turn blue at the touch when the air is damp; when the air is dry they become only tinged with blue.

TUBES Rather long. Attached to the stalk, sometimes completely and sometimes only partially. Light olive yellow in color.

STALK Varies in length and thickness. Sometimes it is cylindrical with a pointed base; occasionally it is cylindrical but swelling about midpoint. Hazel or brown in color, but the color of the base is similar to that of the cap. Fibrillose. Finely velveted and almost covered with furfuraceous matter. It becomes glabrous. Solid and full.

FLESH Hard in the young fungus, but soft in the mature fungus. Whitish with yellowish patches. The flesh immediately under the cuticle of the cap and that of the stalk are brownish. The flesh surrounding the tubes turns a pale sky blue when the air is damp. The odor is faint, and the taste is pleasant.

Boletus (Xerocomus) badius (Bay Boletus)

GOOD   When immature; then inferior. Discard the viscid cap cuticle. Since the cuticle leaves almost indelible spots one should wear gloves when removing it.

HABITAT   Summer and autumn, and occasionally as early as spring. In hardwood and coniferous forests, particularly in pine forests. Especially on grassy sandy ground. Gregarious, it often grows in large numbers. Fruiting bodies may appear four or five times a year.

CAP   Hemispherical or somewhat conical, then convex, then pincushion-shaped, and finally rather plane, occasionally with a slightly pronounced umbo in the center. From 1½-4 inches in diameter. The margin is turned under toward the tubes at first but later turns back in the opposite direction The cuticle is glutinous, shiny, and easily detached from the flesh of the cap. It may be rusty brown, yellowish brown, ochre, or some intermediate color. As the fungus matures, the color becomes paler.

PORES   Small and angular. In the immature fungus the pores exude milky drops. Sulphurous yellow.

TUBES   Short, adnexed to the stalk. Greenish yellow.

STALK   Cylindrical or very irregular in shape. Lemon yellow or whitish in color. The upper part is covered with yellow or cream-colored granules that later turn brown. Near the tubes it exudes milky drops that turn brownish in color. Solid and full.

FLESH   Tender. Yellowish, it does not change color on exposure to the air. The odor and taste are pleasant.

Boletus (Suillus) granulatus (Granulated Boletus)

128 BOLETUS LUTEUS
SUILLUS LUTEUS

GOOD As long as the fungus is immature; the mature fungus is inferior. It should be picked when the grass is not damp with dew. The cuticle of the cap should be removed. In the mature fungus one should also discard the cap margin, the tubes, and the stalk from the ring down.

HABITAT Autumn. Near pines that are at least 10-15 years old; in grass. Fruiting bodies appear only once a year.

CAP Hemispherical, then plane-convex, sometimes with an umbo in the center, and finally pincushion-shaped. From 2-4 inches in diameter. The cuticle is smooth, viscid, thick, and easily detached from the flesh of the cap. Chocolate brown in color with violet-brown radial striation. As the fungus matures the cap color fades.

PORES Small and angular; then dentellate. Yellow, becoming darker.

TUBES Rather long. Adnexed to the stalk. Pale golden yellow in color.

STALK Cylindrical and thick. Above the ring it is pale yellow or off-white and covered with brown granules; beneath the ring it has violet-gray patches. Later the stalk turns brownish. Hard and full.

RING Ample. Off-white at first with violet tinges, later turning brownish. The upper margin is glutinous and the same color as the cap. The lower margin is irregularly torn. It gradually disappears and sticks to the stalk.

FLESH Tender. Off-white or lemon yellow in color. It does not turn blue on exposure to the air. The odor is mild. The taste is barely perceptible.

Boletus (Suillus) luteus (Yellow-brown Boletus)

BOLETUS ELEGANS
SUILLUS ELEGANS

(Elegant Boletus)

GOOD   As long as the fungus is immature; then it becomes inferior. It should be picked in dry weather and when the grass is not dewy. The viscid cuticle of the cap should be removed. In mature specimens, the cap margin, tubes, and the stalk below the ring should also be discarded.

HABITAT   Summer and autumn. In mountains and plains. Under larches. In groups or rows following the arrangement of the larch roots.

CAP   Hemispherical or campanulate; then expanded into the shape of a round pincushion, sometimes with a broad but slightly pronounced umbo in the center. From 1½-5½ inches in diameter. The margin remains curved under toward the tubes for a long time. The cuticle is covered with a glutinous membrane that can be removed. It is golden yellow, orange, or orange-brown in color and often has rust-colored patches.

PORES   Small. Round at first, becoming angular. Sulphurous yellow, turning olive. When crushed between the fingers, the pores turn brown.

TUBES   Short. Adnexed to the stalk and quite decurrent. Sulphurous yellow in color, turning olive. They turn pinkish gray at the touch.

STALK   Cylindrical. Often squat at the base. Solid. The bright yellow color grows stronger in intensity toward the lower part of the stalk. There is darker reticulation above the ring; below the ring the stalk is striate or has dark points. The base is brownish or blackish olive. Stuffed and fibrous.

RING   Membranous. Thin. White, turning yellowish. Fragile. Occasionally part remains attached to the cap margin. Often it disappears leaving behind a brownish annular zone.

FLESH   Firm, turning soft and spongy. Yellow. When exposed to the air it becomes marbled with pink or pinkish brown. The odor is barely noticeable. The taste is slightly acid.

Boletus (Suillus) elegans (Elegant Boletus)

EDIBLE Mediocre. Discard the cap cuticle, which is sticky.

HABITAT From spring till autumn. In mountain and plain. Under larch trees.

CAP Hemispherical or campanulate, then convex or plane. Only rarely does it have a broad but slightly pronounced central umbo. From 1½-5 inches in diameter. The margin curves under toward the tubes; then it withdraws and sometimes preserves pieces of the partial veil. Sometimes the surface is covered with broad shallow depressions that make the surface take on the appearance of thumbprinted dough. The cuticle is sticky, slightly wrinkly, and easily detached from the flesh of the cap. Sometimes, when the air is dry, it becomes slightly scaly. Light ashy color, greenish-ashy, brownish-ashy, yellowish, or even off-white. As the fungus matures the cap becomes patched with reddish brown.

PORES Large and unequal. Angular and dentellate. Off-white, turning violet gray and finally brownish.

TUBES Very long. Sometimes they are round toward the stem, to which they are barely adnexed. Occasionally the tubes are decurrent along the stalk. Grayish, turning violet gray.

STALK Cylindrical. Sometimes squat, sometimes slender. The area above the ring is greenish white, and when the fungus is mature it is covered with brownish furfuraceous matter. The area below the ring is ashen in color, turning greenish gray, then brownish. It is sticky and bears occasional flocculi that are darker than the stalk. Full.

RING Membranous. Thin. Ample. White. It does not last and often ends as a brown zone not even completely circling the stalk.

FLESH The flesh of the young fungus is very firm; that of the mature fungus is soft and watery. It spoils easily. White, but that of the stalk is yellow. The flesh of the cap turns brownish gray when exposed to the air, while that of the base becomes brownish yellow. Here and there it may also turn light blue or green. The odor is pleasant and so is the taste.

Boletus viscidus (Viscid Boletus)

131 BOLETUS PARASITICUS
XEROCOMUS PARASITICUS

(Parasitic Boletus)

NOT RECOMMENDED

HABITAT It grows as a parasite of the inedible **Scleroderma aurantium** 168, which grows in summer and autumn, in woodlands, dry barren land, and sometimes on old stumps.

CAP Hemispherical at first, then expanding. From 1-3 inches in diameter. Velvety. Shaggy. Brownish yellow in color.

PORES Large and angular. Unequal. They join together on the stalk to form small gills that are decurrent. Pale lemon-yellow in color.

TUBES Rather short. Attached to the stalk and later somewhat decurrent. The color ranges from golden to brownish yellow.

STALK Cylindrical. Curving and narrowing at the base Usually long and very thin, but it may occasionally be rather squat. Striate. Velvety. The upper part is ochre yellow, while the lower part is brown with reddish striation.

FLESH Fibrous. Lemon yellow. Mild odor and taste.

Boletus (Xerocomus) parasiticus (Parasitic Boletus)

GOOD   As long as the fungus is young. Discard at least the base of the stalk. It should be boiled first. It may be served raw, but only in small quantities, cut up and seasoned with oil, salt, and pepper as a garnish.

HABITAT   Summer and autumn. In mountainous regions; rarely in the plains. In coniferous woods, especially in pinewoods. In large groups of clusters of two or three specimens that are joined to a single base. The caps of the single clusters may also be joined. Rare in the United States.

CAP   Convex, then plane, irregular, and gibbose. From 1 1/2-4 inches in diameter. The margin is thin, irregularly lobed, undulate, and puckered. White, turning lemon yellow, and finally somewhat ochraceous with lemon-yellow patches. As the fungus matures, the cuticle of the cap dries and splits into rectangular pieces against a lighter ground.

PORES   Small, almost round. White, turning lemon yellow.

TUBES   Very short. Decurrent along the stalk. White, turning lemon yellow.

STALK   Cylindrical or inverted cone in shape. Short and very irregular. Usually it is not central to the cap but off-center. Compact. White, developing lemon-yellow spots. Covered with furfuraceous matter.

FLESH   Firm and fragile. White, turning lemon yellow. The odor is pleasant. It has a taste of almonds.

Good

Polyporus (Scutiger) ovinus (Sheep Polyporus)

133 POLYPORUS CONFLUENS
SCUTIGER CONFLUENS

EDIBLE WITH CAUTION   As long as the fungus is immature. When the fungus is mature its taste remains bitter even after long cooking. Discard the cuticle and the tubes; they are the bitterest parts. To remove the cuticle and tubes, the fungus must be peeled with a sharp knife. Before seasoning and cooking the fungus, it should be boiled in unsalted water for about ten minutes. This cooking water is bitter to the taste and should be discarded. As the flesh cooks it turns flesh pink in color. A large serving will have a strongly purgative effect. It can be dried.

HABITAT   Summer and autumn. In the mountains, rarely in the plains. In coniferous woods. On sandy ground. In moss. It grows in clusters of several individuals the bases of which are joined in one. The cluster is from 6-20 inches in diameter.

CAPS   Spheroid or hemispherical, then expanded in various forms, generally resembling overlapping twisted fans. The individual fungus caps are from 2-6 inches in diameter. The margin is curved under toward the tubes; it becomes lobed and undulate. The cuticle is smooth and can only be removed from the cap flesh by peeling the fungus as if it were a potato. The cuticle of the mature fungus breaks up into several polygonal pieces. The caps are yellowish pink, ochraceous pink, or hazel in color.

PORES   Quite minute and round when the fungus is young, but as the fungus matures the pores widen, retain their round shape, and become fringed. White, turning cream colored and finally assuming the color of the cap.

TUBES   Short and decurrent along the stalk. Off-white or yellowish white.

STALKS   Cylindrical and irregular in shape. Very short; frequently the individual stems cannot be easily distinguished from each other. Central, off-center, or lateral to the caps. The bases fuse into a single mass. Off-white with occasional pink tinges, particularly around the base. Smooth and covered with furfuraceous matter. Firm, fragile, and full.

FLESH   Compact, fragile; soft when full of water but hard when dry. White, it does not change color on exposure to the air. If it does, it only turns faintly pink. The odor is almost unnoticeable. The taste of young specimens is acidulous or bitterish; the taste of mature specimens is very bitter.

Edible with caution

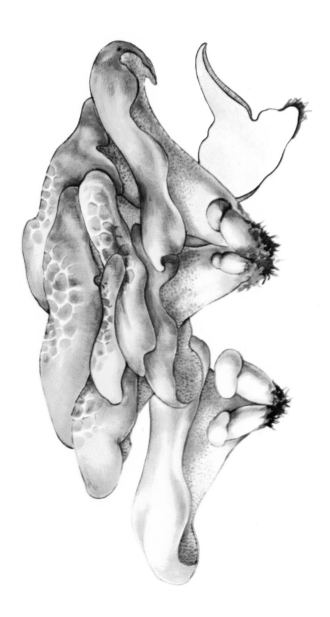

Polyporus (Scutiger) confluens

EDIBLE WITH CAUTION As long as the fungus is totally immature. As soon as it develops it becomes tough and leathery, but even the young fungus is hard to digest. Further, it disagrees with some people.

HABITAT Spring and summer, rarer in autumn. In coniferous and hardwood forests, particularly the latter. On trunks and stumps, dead or live.

CAP Fleshy at first, becoming tough and finally woody. It may take the form of a horseshoe or fan as well as other totally strange shapes. There is a depression where the cap joins the stalk. From 4-16 inches in diameter. The margin is tightly curled under toward the tubes and only slowly uncurls. Light hazel yellow in color and completely covered with brown scales arranged in more or less concentric zones.

PORES Small at first, then large, flattened, angular, and dentellate. Whitish, turning light hazel.

TUBES Short and decurrent along the stalk. They cannot be detached from the cap. Off-white, turning cream colored or light hazel.

STALK Cylindrical and thick, Short and laterally attached to the cap. Only rarely is the stalk central to the cap. The upper half is covered with pore reticulation. Where the pores end there is sometimes a whitish ring-like zone. Below this zone the color is brown, turning blackish. At first the stalk is covered with tobacco-colored furfuraceous matter, but later it becomes glabrous.

FLESH Hard and elastic at first, becoming tough and leathery. In the end it has the consistency of wood. The flesh of the young fungus is white. It does not change color when cut or broken. It has an odor of honey and a pleasant taste.

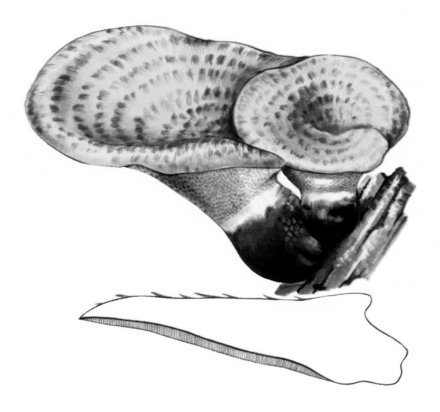

Polyporus squamosus (Dryad's Saddle)

INEDIBLE   When the fungus is mature.

EDIBLE   The margin of young specimens is excellent.

HABITAT   From the middle of spring until the beginning or middle of autumn. In hardwood and coniferous forests, albeit less common in coniferous forests. On trunks. It grows in clusters with a single base. The cluster may be from 4-16 inches in diameter. This fungus completely hollows out the trunk on which it lives and makes it collapse.

CAPS   The caps take the form of a tongue or fan and are gibbose. The margin is almost always undulate, lobed, and broken by deep radial grooves. Sometimes the caps take on the appearance of limp gloves. They extend horizontally outward. Overlapping each other, they often take on bizarre forms. They may be yellow in color, orange yellow, or lemon yellow. As they mature the color fades. They are covered with fine cream-colored furfuraceous matter that increases as the fungus matures.

PORES   Small and rounded, becoming serrate. Sulphurous yellow.

TUBES   Short. They extend as far as the connection of one cap with another. Yellow.

STALK   Most of the time the stalk is absent, and there is only one base joining the fungi of a single cluster. This base is whitish, turning yellowish.

FLESH   Thick. Soft as cheese at first, juicy and exuding amber-yellow drops. Yellowish or whitish with a pleasant odor and an acidulous taste. But as the fungus matures the flesh becomes hard, light, and fragile.

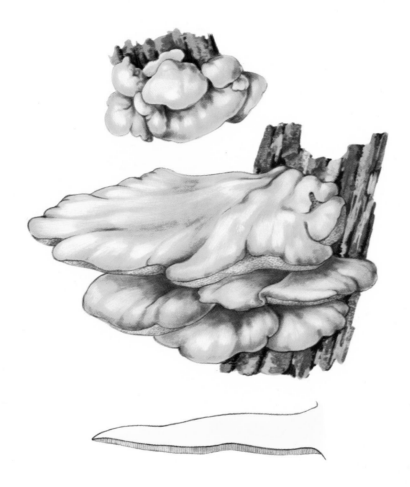

Polyporus (Laetiporus) sulphureus (Chicken Mushroom)

136 POLYPORUS BETULINUS
PIPTOPORUS BETULINUS

INEDIBLE   At first the flesh is elastic and tough; then it becomes corky.

HABITAT   Summer. In damp woodlands. On old and young birches. It rapidly destroys the trees on which it grows.

CAP   It has the form of a semi-circular-edged adze or kidney. It extends horizontally on a short stem from a birch branch or trunk. From 3-6½ inches in diameter. The upper surface is convex, while the lower surface is almost always concave. The margin is curled under toward the tubes and does not uncurl. The cuticle is smooth and thin and easily detached from the cap. As the fungus matures the cuticle cracks and splits. It may be off-white in color, ashy, gray, yellowish, brownish, or reddish. As the fungus matures the cap color fades.

PORES   Small, roundish, and white.

TUBES   Rather short and close. Rigid and easily detached from the flesh of the cap. Whitish.

STALK   Short or absent. Horizontal.

FLESH   Elastic and springy, becoming corky. Whitish. When properly cut it can be used to sharpen razors.

Polyporus (Piptoporus) betulinus (Birch Polyporus)

137 POLYPORUS FRONDOSUS POLYPILUS FRONDOSUS

(Hen of the Woods; Frondose Polyporus)

GOOD As long as the fungus is young. Rather hard. Discard the stalk. It should be cooked well over a low flame.

HABITAT Summer and autumn. In hardwood forests. On old oak, chestnut, hornbeam, yoke-elm and ironwood, and other hardwood stumps. A dangerous parasite. It grows in large clusters from a single base. Numerous stalks grow from a single white base, and these short stalks are attached laterally to their caps. A cluster may be from 6-14 inches in diameter.

CAPS Fleshy but thin. Spatula- or fan-shaped. From 3/4-2½ inches in diameter. The margin is undulate and lobed or dentellate. The surface is delicately tufted and velvety and covered with fine furfuraceous matter. Rugose. Gray, brown-gray, or smoky brown in color.

PORES Small. Round at first but tending to form zones of irregularly shaped pores. White. When crushed between the fingers they turn black.

TUBES Short. They grow only as far as the juncture of one specimen with another. Whitish.

STALKS Most of the time the stalk is totally lacking, and the caps of a single cluster are all attached laterally to the same base. When there are stalks they are white and branching.

FLESH Very fibrous. Fragile. White. The odor and taste are pleasant.

Polyporus (Polypilus) frondosus (Hen of the woods)

POLYPORUS UMBELLATUS (Umbellate Polyporus)
POLYPILUS UMBELLATUS

GOOD   When immature.

HABITAT   Summer. In hardwood forests, especially oak and beech. Generally on tree stumps, but sometimes on the ground. In large clusters that resemble leafless flowering shrubs. They grow year after year in the same place. The cluster may be from 8-16 inches in diameter.

CAPS   Fleshy but thin. Convex with an umbo in the center; becoming plane with a central depression. From 3/4-2 ½ inches in diameter. The margin is thin, undulate, and sometimes radially split. Light gray, brownish gray, or hazel in color. It has darker scales.

PORES   Medium in size. Round, becoming angular. White.

TUBES   Short and decurrent along the stalk. Whitish.

STALK   Resembling tree branches. Cylindrical and fairly long. Sometimes bifurcate. Growing from a single base. White.

FLESH   Thin and tender. Somewhat fibrous. White. It has an odor of dough, but the flesh decomposes rapidly and then exhales a foul odor. The taste is pleasant when the flesh is fresh.

Polyporus (Polypilus) umbellatus (Umbellate Polyporus)

EDIBLE Discard the bitterish-tasting stalk. Boiling the fungus before preparing it for consumption will remove most of the bitter taste, even from the stalk. Inferior.

HABITAT Summer and autumn. In coniferous and hardwood forests, particularly in pine woods.

CAP Roundish, then convex, and finally plane, sometimes with a depression in the center. The cap is gibbose and often irregular in shape. From 2-4½ inches in diameter. The margin is thin and curled under toward the tubes. It is undulate and rather lobed. The surface is smooth at first, becoming wrinkly and split. Smoky gray or smoky brown in color.

PORES Large, irregular, oblong or angular, and sometimes dentellate. White, turning pale ash.

TUBES Very short and decurrent along the stalk. Ashy gray in color.

STALK Cylindrical, it may be long or short. The form is very irregular. Solid and not completely central to the cap. The color is the same as that of the cap or sometimes lighter with whitish or yellowish patches. Covered with light down or very delicate scales. It later becomes glabrous. Stuffed.

FLESH Thick, compact, and very fragile. Fibrous. White but turning ashy pink on exposure to the air. The odor is barely noticeable. The taste of the cap is pleasant, while that of the stalk is bitterish.

Polyporus leucomelas

140 POLYPORUS PES-CAPRAE
SCUTIGER PES-CAPRAE

GOOD   When the fungus is immature. Discard the stem and the cap cuticle. It is best cooked on a grill with salt, pepper, butter, and at the end, parsley.

HABITAT   Summer and autumn. In fir forests. In open areas. Among patches of moss.

CAP   Convex, then flattened or split by a deep diametrical or radial groove. From 2¼-4¾ inches in diameter. The thin margin is curled under toward the tubes. The margin is usually smooth but may be very lobed. The cap is completely covered with well-defined scales arranged with some regularity of pattern and brown in color. The cuticle is greenish, but the general color of the cap is brownish because of the scales.

PORES   Large, decurrent, and yellowish white.

TUBES   Short, decurrent, and yellowish white.

STALK   Squat and irregular in form. When the cap is split by diametrical or radial grooves, the stalk is also split more or less markedly by the continuation of the cap split. Smooth and yellowish.

FLESH   White with greenish tinges. The odor and taste are agreeable.

Good

Polyporus (Scutiger) pes-caprae

INEDIBLE It does not spoil when kept in a dry place and may serve as a curious ornamental knick-knack.

HABITAT Summer and autumn. In woodlands, specially oak and chestnut. Near trees, on old stumps and dead roots.

CAP Circular. The thin margin is sometimes quite undulate. The surface is divided into circular stepped zones arranged around the point at which the cap joins the stem. Covered with a shining crust that may be violaceous or reddish brown, occasionally blackish or even yellowish in color. It has radial striation. From 2-4 inches in diameter.

PORES Small and white, turning yellowish and finally brownish.

TUBES Short, becoming quite long. White, turning yellowish.

STALK Cylindrical and quite irregular in shape. Long. It is of the same color as the cap, to which it is laterally attached.

FLESH Elastic, then tough, and finally corky.

Ganoderma lucidum (Shining Polyporus)

GOOD When the fungus is young. It can be sliced and cooked in the same manner as a beefsteak. But even when cooked the flavor is quite acidulous, so it is not to everyone's taste. It is generally more pleasing when served raw in salad mixed with greens. In this way it retains its vitamin C content, which amounts to 150 milligrams per hundred grams of fungus.

HABITAT Summer and autumn. In hardwood forests. On old trees and on stumps of even recently chopped chestnut, oak, beech, and other hardwoods.

CAP Very fleshy. When it is fully developed it resembles a tongue or a rounded adze protruding horizontally. From 4-8 inches in length and from 3/4-2½ inches in thickness. The thin margin is often lobed. The surface is liverish red. At first, however, it is covered with yellowish papillae and seems orange red. Then it becomes velvety and finally takes on a gelatinous appearance together with its markedly liverish coloring, especially along the margin.

PORES They do not form at once but only when the fungus is quite developed. Small and round. Cream colored or yellowish, turning pink. When crushed they turn brownish in color.

TUBES They do not form at once but only when the fungus is well along in its development. Short and thin, tender and fleshy. They are not joined to each other but free in the manner of brush bristles. They are set quite closely together however. Decurrent along the stalk when it is distinguishable from the cap. Yellowish or cream colored.

STALK It may be absent. When there is a stalk it is laterally attached to the cap margin. Cylindrical, squat, and sticky. Yellowish or pinkish yellow.

FLESH Thick. Light or dark red and grooved with lighter veining running from the base of the fungus toward the cap margin. When squeezed it produces a fluid that resembles pale blood. The odor is slight and the taste is pleasantly acidulous.

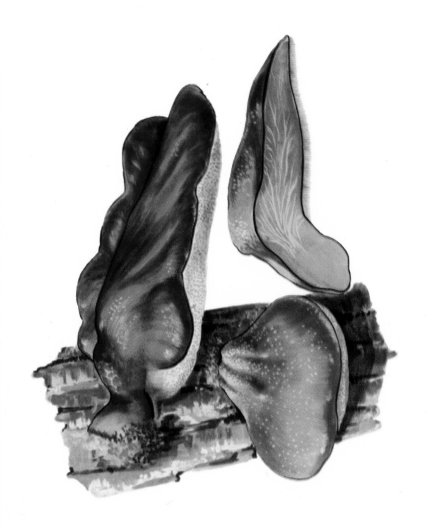

Fistulina hepatica (Beefsteak Mushroom)

(White Jelly Mushroom)

EDIBLE   Even when raw, but better cooked.

HABITAT   From August to November. In coniferous woods. On old stumps. Frequently in clusters with overlapping caps.

CAP   The form varies considerably, but most often it resembles an oyster or a roundish disc; it may assume altogether strange shapes. From 1-2 inches in diameter. It grows horizontally from the host stump. The margin is thin, lobed, and often very irregularly undulate. The surface is translucent and covered with papillae. The color varies from silvery whitish, to ashy, to pale brownish gray.

ACULEI   The lower face of the cap is covered with small prickles known as aculei and there are neither gills nor pores. The aculei are close, short, white, gelatinous, diaphanous, and very decurrent along the stalk.

STALK   Sometimes it amounts simply to a base by which the cap is attached to the stump that hosts the fungus, but sometimes it is distinct from the cap. Then it is cylindrical, moderately long, and often rather curved. It is made of the same substance as the cap. White at first, turning ashy; lighter than the cap.

FLESH   Soft, elastic, jelly and diaphanous-like gelatin. The odor is slight, and the taste is pleasant and resiny.

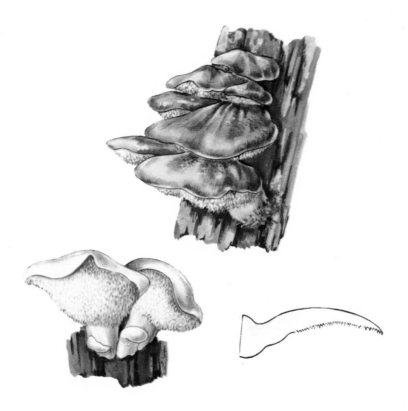

Pseudohydnum gelatinosum (White Jelly Mushroom)

EXCELLENT When young. It cooks quickly. When it is very mature, it is leathery and very bitter in taste. Discard the stalk. Before preparing it with seasonings it should be boiled for a few minutes. The water in which the mushroom is cooked should be thrown away to eliminate all traces of bitterness. It is almost always found intact, without larvae or young snails.

HABITAT From the end of summer till the beginning of winter. In coniferous and hardwood forests, particularly beech, oak, hornbeam, yoke-elm and ironwood. In damp places. It grows in large rings or very long rows. Occasionally two or more specimens share a common base, and sometimes the caps are partially joined.

CAP Convex and gibbose, then plane-convex, always irregular in form and sometimes somewhat concave. From 1-5 inches in diameter. The margin is often irregular, lobed, and undulate. The surface is yellowish white, light hazel, pale rust, or light orange-brown in color. It is not translucent. Velvety.

ACULEI The lower surface of the cap is not covered with gills or tubes but with stiff aculei. Close and rather long, depending on the age of the fungus. Decurrent along the stalk. Very fragile. White, gradually turning the color of the cap.

STALK Cylindrical and squat. With irregular swelling. Sometimes it is not central to the cap, but more or less off-center. Sometimes it has a very bulbous base. It grows deep in the ground, and the fruiting body may reappear several times in the same season. One should be careful not to pull up this base from the ground but to leave it there. One should cut the fungus stalk at the surface of the ground. The color is white at first, but it gradually turns the color of the cap. Compact and full.

FLESH Thick, firm, and very resilient. White, turning yellowish or brown on contact with the air. The odor is pleasant. The taste is acidulous and, in mature specimens, rather bitter.

MISTAKEN HARMLESSLY For the variety **rufescens**, which is also edible but smaller and more delicate; hazel pink or pale orange-hazel in color.

Excellent

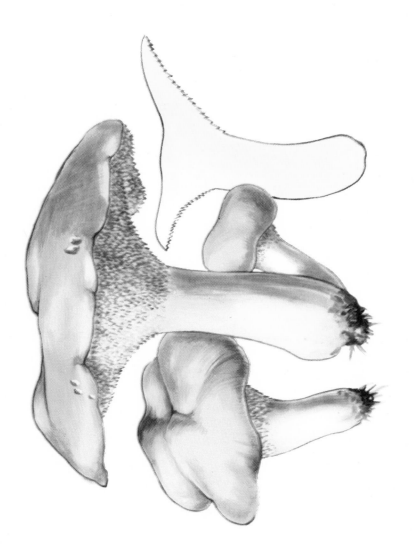

Hydnum (Dentinum) repandum (Spreading Hydnum)

EDIBLE When the fungus is young. Take a sharp knife and remove the scales that cover the cap; scrape the aculei off the lower surface of the cap. Boil the fungus first and throw out the water to remove the bitter taste. Even with this preparation, it is not to every taste. It is advisable therefore to cut the fungus into small slices and dry it. Then it can be cooked in a saucepan as a seasoning for roast meat. A small handful is enough because this fungus is very savory. It can also be kept in oil after it has been boiled, and it is excellent this way.

HABITAT From the end of summer until the beginning of winter. In plains or mountainous regions. In coniferous woods, especially under fir trees or in open oak woods. Gregarious, it grows in semi-circles or rows.

CAP Convex with a central depression, then flattened with a deeper central depression, and finally funnel-shaped. From 2¼-7 inches in diameter. The margin curls under toward the aculei and often remains curled even when the fungus is mature. The cuticle is light hazel gray but completely covered with large brown scales. The color that results is a kind of smoky brown. The scales are arranged in concentric circles and grow coarser and thicker toward the center. As the fungus ages the scales disappear, except at the center.

ACULEI The lower face of the cap is covered with stiff aculei instead of gills or tubes. The aculei are close, regular, and decurrent along the stalk. Very fragile. Ashy at first, but turning bluish ashy in color.

STALK Cylindrical and squat. It is sometimes eccentric to the cap. The base may be very bulbous. Smooth but fibrillose. Yellowish, turning brownish gray with bluish tinges at the base. Hollow. In the mature fungus the hollow of the stalk is continuous with the funnel-form of the cap. In the mature fungus, the stalk is almost always wormy.

FLESH Firm and white, turning grayish. Almost odorless. The taste is bitterish.

Hydnum imbricatum (Imbricated Hydnum)

CLAVARIA FORMOSA
RAMARIA FORMOSA

(Formosa Coral; Beautiful Coral)

INEDIBLE Purgative.

HABITAT Late summer and autumn. In coniferous and hardwood forests. In shady damp places. On mossy ground. Gregarious.

GENERAL APPEARANCE It resembles a small coral tree with branches growing straight up. From 3-7 inches in height; from 1½-3½ inches in width.

TRUNK Thick and very long. Sometimes the base ends in a root shape. It often has longitudinal grooves. Hard and white, with pink tinges.

BRANCHES Close and cylindrical. Almost vertical, with branches growing upward. Fragile. Hazel pink, yellowish pink, or orange pink, later turning ochre.

TIPS Minute and lemon yellow in color.

FLESH White with a pinkish tinge. When cut or pressed it may turn wine brown and later smoky brown. Fragile. It has no particlar odor. The taste is very bitter.

MISTAKEN For various other similar species from which it can be distinguished if one is attentive to its special features - pinkish branches and lemon yellow tips.

Clavaria (Ramaria) formosa (Formosa coral)

147 RAMARIA AUREA
CLAVARIA AUREA

(Golden Coral)

EDIBLE   When the fungus is young.

HABITAT   Summer and autumn. In woods, damp places, and in mossy places.

GENERAL APPEARANCE   It resembles a small coral tree with branches growing upward. From 3-7½ inches in height; from 2-3¼ inches in width.

TRUNK   Thick and short. Yellowish or cream colored.

BRANCHES   Numerous, cylindrical, and large. They become very twisted toward the tips. Golden yellow, turning ochraceous yellow.

TIPS   Minute and cylindrical. Truncated, slightly bifurcate, or dentellate. Golden yellow, turning ochraceous yellow.

FLESH   Firm, becoming rather soft. White, but the outer flesh is light yellow in color.

MISTAKEN   For various other species, particularly the **Clavaria (Ramaria) flava** 148, a fungus that is good when young and is distinguished by its white trunk, occasionally patched wine red, and by its lemon yellow branches.

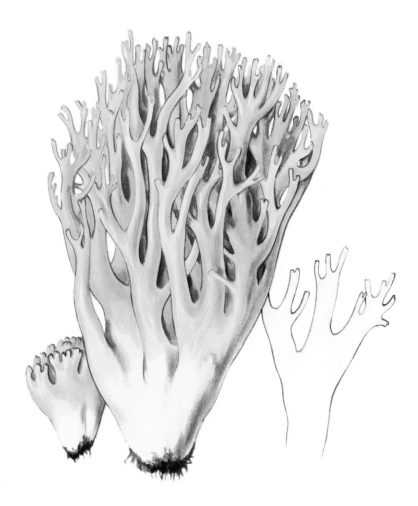

Clavaria (Ramaria) aurea (Golden Coval)

148 RAMARIA FLAVA
CLAVARIA FLAVA

INEDIBLE   As soon as it is fully mature, because of its strong purgative effect.

GOOD   When young. Only the trunk should be cooked; the rest should be discarded. It cooks quickly. Tender. It can also be dried.

HABITAT   Summer and autumn. In coniferous and hardwood forests, particularly beech. In shady and damp places. On mossy ground. Gregarious, it grows in large groups.

GENERAL APPEARANCE   It resembles a small coral tree with branches growing upward. From 2-6 inches in height, and from 2-6 inches in width.

TRUNK   Large and short. Firm and white, with tinges of lemon yellow and wine-red patches, particularly in specimens growing under conifers.

BRANCHES   Numerous. Some start from the base of the trunk. Cylindrical and much flattened. Grooved toward the bottom. Smooth and rigid. Light lemon yellow or lighter or darker sulphurous yellow. The branches are very leathery and tough.

TIPS   Minute and short. Each branch has two or three obtuse tips; rarely dentate. Light lemon yellow in color or lighter or darker sulphurous yellow.

FLESH   Tender and fragile. Watery. White, but becoming tinged a reddish color in mature specimens. The odor is pleasant. The taste of the trunk flesh of young specimens is pleasant, but that of mature specimens is bitterish. The taste of the flesh of the branches is always bitterish.

MISTAKEN   For various other species but chiefly for **Clavaria (Ramaria) aurea** 147, an edible fungus that is golden yellow in color and does not have wine-red patches on the trunk.

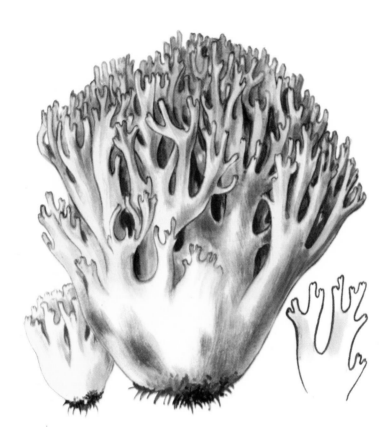

Clavaria (Ramaria) flava (Yellow Coral)

149 CLAVARIA PALLIDA
* RAMARIA MAIREI

POISONOUS   It causes vomiting.

HABITAT   From August to October. In mountainous regions; rarely in the plains. In hardwood forests. In shady damp places. On mossy ground.

GENERAL APPEARANCE   It resembles a small coral tree with branches growing upward. From 3-7 inches in height; from 2-4 inches in width.

TRUNK   Thick and short. Hard. Light brown in color but paler at the base.

BRANCHES   Numerous and close. Almost vertical. Grooved longitudinally. Pale ochraceous cream with violet tinges.

TIPS   Short and thick. Cylindrical, flattened, and bifurcate. Pale violet in the young fungus, later fading in color.

FLESH   Firm and white. The odor is very slight. The taste may be sweetish or bitterish.

MISTAKEN   For various other species, but especially the **Clavaria (Ramaria) botrytis** 150, a good fungus which is reddish only at the tips.

---

* Two **C. pallida** exist in the literature. This one, cited (Bresadola) by the author, was reclassified and given the new specific ephithet **Mairei** by Donk.

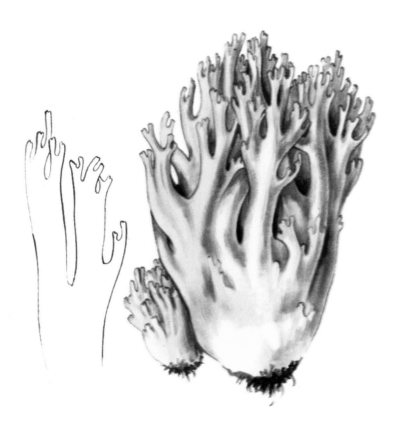

Clavaria pallida (Ramaria Mairei)

150 CLAVARIA BOTRYTIS
RAMARIA BOTHRYTIS

GOOD In the very young fungus; otherwise fibrous and bitterish. It should be boiled for a few minutes before being cooked with seasoning. Only the trunk should be used; the rest should be discarded.

HABITAT Late summer and autumn. In hardwood forests, especially beech; rarely in coniferous woods.

GENERAL APPEARANCE It resembles the flowery part of a cauliflower. From 4-8 inches tall; from 4-8 inches wide.

TRUNK Large and short. Fleshy. The base is slender or rounded. White, turning pale ochre.

BRANCHES Numerous. They start from the trunk and not from the base. Cylindrical and thick. Unequal. Very rugose. White, turning pale ochre.

TIPS Short, minute, and bidented. Pink or violet pink in color.

FLESH Firm but fragile. White, it does not change color when exposed to the air. The odor is pleasant. The taste may be pleasant or bitterish.

MISTAKEN For various other species, especially for **Ramaria Mairie** 149, a poisonous fungus, which has not only violet-colored tips but also branches and the upper part of the trunk suffused with a pale violet color.

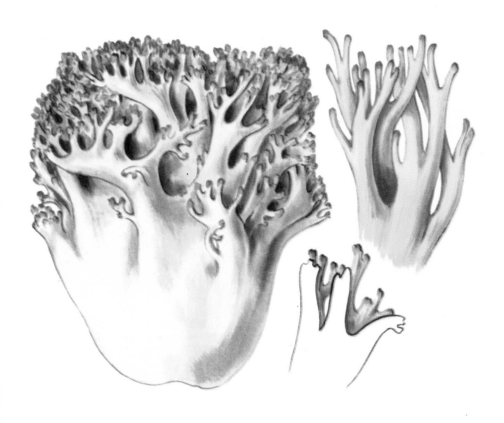

Clavaria (Ramaria) botrytis (Purple-tipped Coral)

EDIBLE As long as the fungus is totally immature. Nevertheless it is inferior in quality. Before preparing it with seasoning, it should first be boiled for a few minutes and the water thrown out.

HABITAT Summer and autumn. In hardwood and coniferous forests. More common in hardwood than in coniferous forests. Gregarious or solitary.

GENERAL APPEARANCE It resembles a club or a pestle. From 2 1/2-9 1/2 in height; the diameter of the trunk is from 3/4-2 1/2 inches. Sometimes it is smooth but more often wrinkly. Yellow, turning ochre, then brick or rust colored; with violaceous tinges. The base is covered with down or else it is glabrous.

FLESH Fibrous or spongy. Tough. White or yellowish but turning vinaceous brown on exposure to the air. The odor is faint. The taste is sweetish at first but ultimately becomes very sharp.

N. B. The illustration on the facing page also depicts **Clavaria truncata**, an edible flat-topped fungus.

Clavaria (Clavariadelphus) pistillaris
(Large-clubbed Clavaria)

152 NEUROPHYLLUM CLAVATUM
GOMPHUS CLAVATUS

EDIBLE   As long as the fungus is young. Later it turns acid and is indigestible.

HABITAT   Summer and autumn. In mountainous regions. In coniferous forests, particularly fir. It also grows in hardwood forests, especially beech. On the stumps of dead trees. On mossy ground. In rows, rings, and large groups. It may also grow in clusters.

GENERAL APPEARANCE   At first it resembles a small truncated club, flattened at the top. Later it resembles a more or less hollow spinning top, or a fan rounded into conical shape. One side is thick and the opposite is thin, almost membranous and open. From 2 1/4-4 3/4 inches in height; the greatest diameter is from 1 1/2-3 inches. The margin is thin, lobed, and puckered. The inner surface is violet, turning ochre and finally olive. The outer surface is violet pink and smooth at first; then it becomes nervate, branching, reticulate, and darker in color.

STALK   Often the stalk is nothing more than a base connecting the fungus to the ground. Usually short and squat, it may sometimes be rather long. Smooth and full. Pale violet in color, becoming still lighter as the fungus matures.

FLESH   Tender and white. An odor of almonds. The taste is pleasant but becomes quite acid when the fungus is mature.

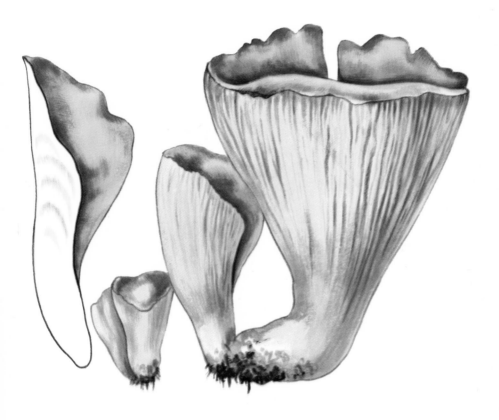

Neurophyllum clavatum (Clustered Chanterelle)
Gomphus clavatus

GOOD Discard very mature or spoiled specimens. It requires long cooking. It is not attacked by larvae. Once cooked it can be kept for a long time without spoiling.

HABITAT From June till October. In all woods. It is found especially after heavy rains. On dead leaves and mossy ground. It grows in large groups, often arranged in rings.

CAP Convex and sometimes knotty; then depressed; and finally funnel-shaped. From 1-3½ inches in diameter. The margin is irregularly lobed and puckered. At first the surface is velvety, but it later becomes glabrous and dry. Golden yellow or orange yellow in color. There are several varieties with different coloration.

PSEUDO-GILLS Instead of true gills there are folds or veinings along the lower surface of the cap. These pseudo-gills are large, branching, and very decurrent along the stalk. They are the same color as the cap.

STALK It has the form of an inverted cone. Of the same color as the cap. Full and fibrous.

FLESH Tough and fibrous. Yellow on the outside but paler inside. It has a pleasant odor of apricot. The taste is quite sharp when mature.

MISTAKEN For the poisonous **Clitocybe olearia** 64 which has genuine gills that are well defined, close, thin, and reddish orange in color, as well as a stalk that is brown at first, turning blackish.

N. B. In the illustration on the facing page are depicted various **Cantharelli**: **cibarius**, above center; **cibarius** in the variety **neglectus** to the left of the preceding; **cibarius** of the variety **amethysteus**, a young specimen, below left; **cibarius** of the variety **albus**, young specimen, below right; **cinereus**, right and above the preceding. They are all edible.

Cantharellus cibarius (Chanterelle)

GOOD Somewhat hard.

HABITAT From August to November, In mountainous regions. In hardwood and coniferous forests, especially fir and pine. In damp places. In large groups and sometimes in clusters.

CAP More membranous than fleshy. Funnel-shaped. From 1-3 inches in diameter. At first the base of the funnel is closed; later it is open and continuous with the stalk cavity. The margin has oddly puckered lobes. The inner surface is at first covered with flocculi darker in color than the cuticle; later it becomes glabrous and grooved with striation. The color is brownish gray, turning brown. The outer surface is continuous with the stalk cuticle. It is smooth at first and later grooved with veining or pseudo-gills, slight, branching, distant, and very decurrent along the stalk. Orange yellow or pink in color.

STALK It narrows toward the base, but occasionally the base is very squat. Undulate. Grooved with longitudinal wrinkles. Often compressed here and there. Orange yellow. Completely hollow. In mature specimens the stalk cavity almost always is a continuation of the funnel of the cap.

FLESH Thin and tough. Pale yellow. A slightly fruity odor. The taste is mild.

Good

Cantharellus lutescens (Yellowish Chanterelle)

EDIBLE It was once unjustifiably considered suspect. It should be boiled first.

HABITAT Summer and autumn. In woodlands, particularly pine.

CAP Not fleshy but cartilaginous. Funnel-shaped. From 3/4-2³/₄ inches in diameter. The funnel is frequently open at the bottom and continuous with the stalk cavity. The margin is undulate and covered with fine down. The surface is covered with small scales, darker in color than the rest of the surface. When the air is damp the color is dark brown; when the air is dry, it turns hazel-yellow.

PSEUDO-GILLS Branching. Somewhat decurrent along the stalk. Yellowish, turning bluish gray.

STALK Cylindrical. Sometimes swelling at the base. Occasionally curved and compressed. Without down. Hollow and tube-shaped, continuous with the funnel of the cap. Yellow or brownish yellow.

FLESH Membranous. Yellowish. An earthy or mossy odor. The taste is faint.

N. B. **C. tubaeformis** and **C. infundibuliformis** are often given as synonyms. They are different mushrooms, however, although the differences are not important for the amateur - both are edible.

Cantharellus tubaeformis (Tubaform Chanterelle)

GOOD The flavor is fine, but the fungus is quite hard. It can be dried and powdered and used as seasoning. It remains blackish even when cooked.

HABITAT Summer and autumn. In woods of conifers, but more common in hardwood forests, especially beech. In damp places. On mossy ground. In large and close groups or in dense clusters.

GENERAL APPEARANCE It resembles a hollow cornucopia with its point in the ground. From 2½-7 inches in height; the diameter of the upper aperture is from 2-4 inches. The margin is irregularly lobed and undulate. Inside it is blackish gray in color or brownish gray and covered with small darker scales. Outside it is somewhat lighter. Smooth at first but becoming grooved with nervature or shallow ridges and covered with furfuraceous matter. When the weather is damp the entire fungus seems blackish.

STALK It amounts to nothing more than a base in the ground. Smooth, hollow, and blackish.

FLESH More membranous than meaty. Elastic. Grayish. The odor is mildly unpleasant when the fungus is mature. It is almost without taste.

Craterellus cornucopioides (Horn of Plenty)

GOOD As long as the fungus is not full grown. Later it becomes quite leathery and tough.

HABITAT In September and October. In coniferous woodlands. On the ground near freshly cut tree stumps.

GENERAL APPEARANCE It resembles a cauliflower, yellowish white in color, from 8-20 inches in diameter.

TRUNK Short, broad, globose, gibbose; the base goes far down into the ground and resembles a root. Pale yellow in color with brown or reddish zones.

BRANCHING Starting from the trunk. Flat, fleshy, and thick. The branches spread out fanwise and curl up in funnel shapes that intersect each other irregularly. The margin has rounded, undulate, and wrinkled lobes. Creamy white or pale lemon yellow in color. There are occasional twisting zones that are reddish brown in color. The margin is paler in color.

FLESH That of the branches is elastic, slightly tough, and white, with an aromatic odor of resin, anise, or cinnamon. The taste in nutty at first but then becomes somewhat unpleasant. The flesh of the trunk is white and fibrous.

Good

Sparassis crispa (Cauliflower Mushroom)

INEDIBLE When the fungus is fully mature, it is altogether inedible and gives off a fetid smell. When the fungus is still immature and still has the form of an egg, it is very probably as edible as other species of this genus. One should dig around the mature fungus to find these Stinkhorn "eggs".

HABITAT Summer and autumn in rainy weather. In shrubby woods, in parklands, among hedges, and near tree stumps. Solitary.

GENERAL APPEARANCE At first it resembles a small white egg. When cut in section, it resembles a nut with a yellowish kernel that later turns greenish. Later it takes on the appearance of a tallow candle, from 6-10 inches high. White. The cap resembles a candle snuffer. Hanging from the cap margin, like a cylindrical collar or skirt, is a large-mesh network.

CAP Conical or campanulate but truncated. At the top is a disc-shaped element with a hole in the center. From 1½-2 inches in height, and from 1½-2 inches in diameter. Hollow and thin. The outer surface is irregular and alveolate. It is covered with a glutinous layer that is greenish ochre at first, turning olive green, and becoming even darker. In the end it is blackish. As this glutinous layer blackens it dissolves into a kind of sticky liquid that attracts flies.

NETTING From the cap margin hangs a cylindrical or widening skirt-shaped netting that usually reaches halfway down the stalk. It is whitish and fragile. It gradually dissolves as the fungus matures.

STALK Cylindrical and somewhat swollen about halfway up; conical toward the cap and toward the base. From 4-8 inches in height; the maximum diameter is that of the cap. Pitted, eroded, and spongy. White or off-white. Hollow. The stem walls may be up to 3/8 inch thick.

VOLVA It envelops and almost swathes the base. Full and easily detached. White, pink, or pale ochraceous yellow at first, turning ochre.

FLESH Very fragile. Porous and spongy. White. When the fungus is mature, the flesh gives off a strong fetid odor that can be smelled at some distance and would discourage anyone from sampling the taste of the fungus.

N. B. Other species of **Dictyophorae** grow in woodlands, gardens, and hedges; they may lack the netted collar, but they are just as foul smelling, and they are inedible except, perhaps, in the egg stage.

Dictyophora duplicata (Stinkhorn)

INEDIBLE

HABITAT From spring till autumn. In hardwood forests. In shady and humid hollows. In hedges and under bushes.

GENERAL APPEARANCE At first it is more or less regularly globe-shaped. From 1-2½ inches in diameter. It is attached to the ground by a peduncle that separates into filaments similar to root filaments. From the peduncle small wrinkles or pleats or grooves rise high on the surface of the globe. The outside covering of the globe is whitish. Later this covering, the volva, tears, beginning at the top. Inside it is pink or pinkish yellow. A netting or latticework emerges from the volva and expands like a sphere, finally reaching a diameter of from 2½-5 inches. The meshes of this lattice are polygonal, irregular, broad, and relatively few in number. The braids of this latticework are thick, hollow, and very fragile. They are flattened on the outside. When cut in section they are sometimes rectangular with fairly bright edges. Sometimes the section is lenticular, pinkish brown in color with ochre striping. This striping is transverse to the axis of the braid. On the inner side these braids are rounded. They are red and pitted with small holes that are brownish in the center. Here and there is a green granuloid kind of sticky substance. When this fungus is fully mature it gives off an intolerable stench in marked contrast to the delicacy of its form.

Clathrus cancellatus (Latticed Stinkhorn)

EXCELLENT As long as the inner substance is still white and firm. As soon as it yellows, the fungus is no longer edible. It may be eaten raw in salad or fried in butter.

HABITAT Summer and autumn. In mountainous regions. In sparse woodlands, pastures, along footpaths, and in orchards.

GENERAL APPEARANCE It resembles a more or less compressed ball. From 2-10 inches in diameter but huge specimens have been found weighing many pounds. It is attached to the ground by a small peduncle that has small rootlike filaments growing into the ground. It is enveloped in a double covering. The outer covering is white, turning hazel-white, soft and velvety. Then it becomes smooth and fragile. With age it splits and breaks up into fragments resembling paving tiles. And finally it falls away. The inner covering is off-white, turning yellowish, then grayish and more or less sooty. Thin and very fragile, it splits irregularly from the top as the fungus matures.

INTERNAL SUBSTANCE White and compact, turning yellow and flaccid, then olive brown and mushy, and finally clotted and pulverulent and tobacco brown in color. This powder can be made to spurt out by squeezing the cartilaginous covering. The odor of the young fungus is good; that of the mature fungus is quite nauseating. The taste of the immature fungus is mild and pleasant.

MISTAKEN For various young **Amanitae**, including some poisonous and deadly specimens, when the puffball is very small. But when young Amanitas are cut in half they display a section of the cap, which is more or less colored, and of the stalk.

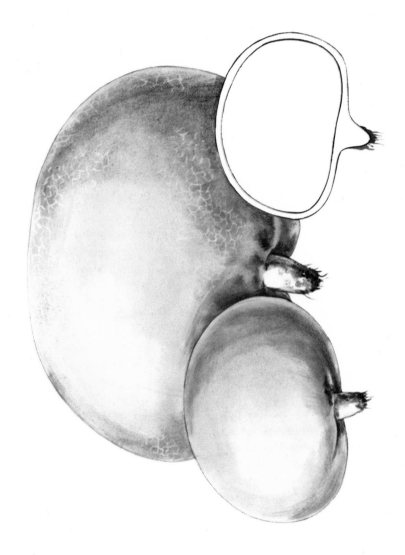

Lycoperdon maximum (Giant Puffball)
Calvatia gigantea

EXCELLENT As long as the substance inside is still white and firm. As soon as it begins to yellow it is no longer edible. It can be eaten raw in salad or fried in butter. Discard the stalk, which is woody.

HABITAT Summer; rarer in autumn. In mountainous regions. In woods and pastures, and along footpaths. In rows.

GENERAL APPEARANCE It resembles an inverted pear. From 2½-5½ inches in diameter. It is enveloped by a double covering. The outer covering is off-white, turning yellow or ashy. In the young fungus, this covering is covered with small sharp flakes. These disappear after a while leaving behind them flattened cottony, truncated pyramids, resembling mosaic tiles. The inner covering does not reach to the base and, in consequence, is compressed and spherical rather than pear-shaped. Whitish, turning yellowish and finally ashy. Fragile, it splits at the top in the shape of a crater mouth with an irregular rim.

INTERNAL SUBSTANCE Compact and white, turning soft and yellowish, then mushy and brownish; finally clotty and pulverulent and tobacco brown in color. This powder may be made to spirt out by pressing the cartilaginous cover. The substance of the base is spongy and grayish. As it dries it becomes felty and continuous with the covering in a tough whole. The odor of the young fungus is good, but that of the mature fungus is very disagreeable. The taste of the young fungus is mild and pleasant.

MISTAKEN For various young Amanitas, including some poisonous and some deadly specimens. But when the young Amanitas are cut one can see the cap, more or less colored, and the stalk in section.

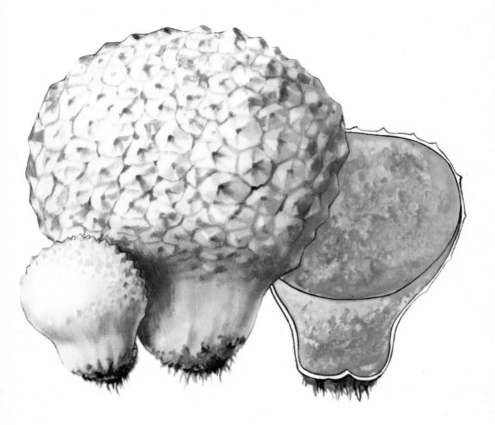

Lycoperdon bovista (Collapsing Puffball)
Calvatia uteriformis

GOOD As long as the fungus is not mature. As soon as the inner substance begins to yellow, the fungus is no longer edible. It can be eaten raw.

HABITAT From the end of summer until the end of autumn. In woodlands. In groups, some quite numerous.

GENERAL APPEARANCE It resembles a spinning top or a small pear with the stem end growing from the ground. There is usually a small umbo on the top. There is no real stalk but simply a short peduncle growing into the ground. From 1-2½ inches in height; from 3/4-1¼ inches in diameter.

OUTER COVERING White at first with a pink tinge. Covered with dense prickles, increasing in number and growing longer toward the top. Fragile and tending to fall off, they are surrounded by smaller and more numerous lasting warts. As the fungus matures, the outer covering becomes yellowish, then brownish gray, and finally breaks open at the top. The pediculate base is almost always free of prickles and warts and is off-white in color.

INNER COVERING It does not extend into the stalk. Off-white in color, turning ashy and opening at the top.

INNER SUBSTANCE At first it is white and firm with a mild odor and a pleasant taste. Then it turns yellow, becomes doughy, soggy, and olive; finally it becomes clotted and pulverulent and begins to come out of the opening formed at the top of the fungus. The inner substance of the stem is whitish and becomes spongy and tough as it dries out.

MISTAKEN For various young Amanitas, including some poisonous and deadly specimens. But when young Amanitas are cut from top to bottom one can see the cap, more or less colored, and the stalk in section.

Good

Lycoperdon perlatum (Gem-studded Puffball)

163 LYCOPERDON SACCATUM

EDIBLE As long as the fungus is young, which is to say, as long as the inner substance remains firm and white. In any case, it is inferior. Discard the stalk, which is woody.

HABITAT Summer and autumn. In coniferous and hardwood forests, in clearings, uncultivated land, and fields. Particularly in the vicinity of poplar, willow, and occasionally oak. Often on mossy ground.

GENERAL APPEARANCE This fungus resembles a champagne cork or a flat onion sitting on a cylindrical cork. One can, therefore, distinguish a cap and a stalk in this fungus. Total height is between 3 and 6½ inches.

CAP The cap peridium is white or smoky white and covered with small needles or granules that later fall off. Then the peridium turns brownish. The inner substance is firm and white at first, becoming yellowish, then olive brown, and finally olive. It then becomes pulverulent and clotted-filamentose. Meanwhile a kind of hemispherical calotte has gradually become detached from the cap, and from the opening thus formed there begins to come out the powder closed inside. Finally this small cartilaginous calotte also falls off.

STALK It may resemble a goatskin bottle or be sac-shaped. Marked by deep folds or grooves, sometimes twisted both at the base and at the junction of the stalk and cap. The covering of the stalk is white or smoky white at first. It is covered with tiny needles or granules that later fall off, and then the stalk appears brownish in color. The inner substance of the stalk is white and very spongy at first; then it becomes totally spongy, with hollows, and turns yellowish.

MISTAKEN For various young Amanitas, including some poisonous and some deadly specimens. But when the young Amanitas are cut one can see the cap, more or less colored, and the stalk in section.

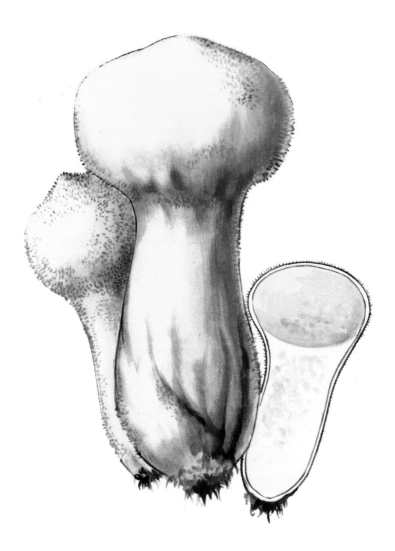

Lycoperdon saccatum (Elongated Puffball)

INEDIBLE

HABITAT Summer and autumn. In coniferous and hardwood forests, especially beech. In damp places. Often in groups of numerous specimens.

GENERAL APPEARANCE This fungus consists of a globular head supported by a short stalk that resembles an inverted cone in shape. The globular head is completely covered with spiny prickles that are sharp, close, and brown. As the fungus matures these aculei fall, revealing a brownish gray surface that is covered with reticulation corresponding to the attachments of the fallen prickles. The outer covering is membranous and very thick.

INNER SUBSTANCE Firm and white at first and enveloped in a second covering thinner than the outer covering. It turns yellowish, then brownish. It become pulverulent and then begins to issue from the small crater-like opening that has formed at the top of the covering itself. The substance of the short stalk is spongy; whitish in color at first, it turns yellow.

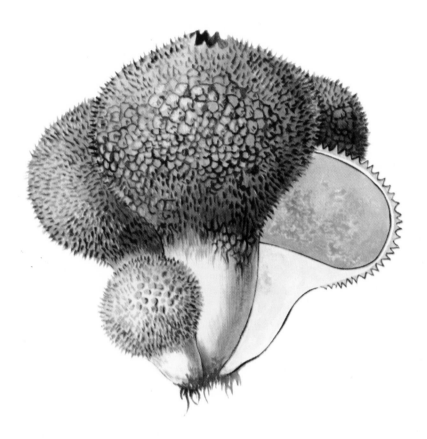

Lycoperdon echinatum

EDIBLE As long as it is very large and still young. As soon as the inner substance turns yellowish, the fungus is no longer edible.

HABITAT Autumn. In woods. On rotten stumps, especially beech. But also on damp sandy ground and in the grass. Frequently in numerous clusters.

GENERAL APPEARANCE It resembles a small inverted pear or a spinning top. Total height is between 3/4 and 3 inches. Occasionally there is a small umbo on the top. The base on the stump or ground tapers down. The outer covering is yellowish at first and covered with minute reddish-brown warts. As the fungus matures these warts fall off, revealing a yellowish surface that later turns smoky yellow and is divided into small sections resembling polygonal tiles and darker in color.

INNER SUBSTANCE Firm and white at first and enveloped in a second covering thinner than the outer one. The inner substance first turns greenish yellow, then olive brown and soggy. Finally it becomes pulverulent and tobacco brown in color and begins to emerge from the small opening that has meanwhile appeared at the top of the covering.

MISTAKEN For various young **Amanitae**, including some poisonous and some deadly specimens. But when the young **Amanitae** are cut one can see the cap, more or less colored, and the stalk in section.

Edible

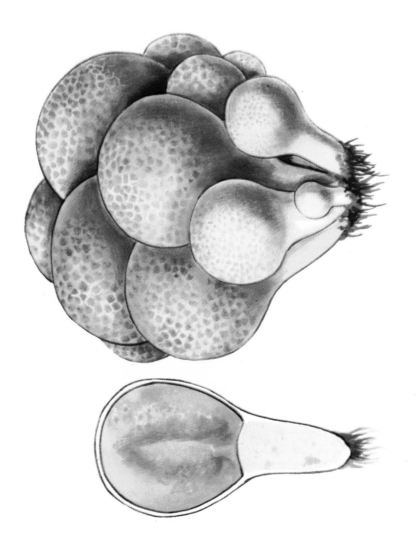

Lycoperdon pyriforme (Pear-shaped Puffball)

EDIBLE When immature. As soon as the inner substance begins to yellow, it is no longer edible. But even before this happens the fungus is inferior.

HABITAT Summer and autumn; occasionally in spring. In fields, pastures, along the edges of footpaths, and in the grass. In dry places. Gregarious.

GENERAL APPEARANCE It is globose or globose-compressed in appearance. From 3/4 to 2¾ inches in diameter. It rests directly on the ground. It has a small underground stem. The inner substance is enveloped in an outer covering that is very thick, membranous, smooth, whitish or smoky white, and fragile. It breaks up as the fungus matures and falls away. A second covering, in direct contact with the inner substance, is as thin as paper but tough. White at first, it turns leaden gray or smoky gray, and finally opens at the top.

INNER SUBSTANCE Firm and white, turning yellowish, then olive brown, and finally tobacco brown. Pulverulent and sometimes very clotted, this substance begins to push out the hole in the top.

MISTAKEN For various young **Amanitae**, including some poisonous and deadly specimens. But when the young **Amanitae** are cut in half one can see the cap, more or less colored, and the stalk in section.

Bovista nigrescens (Round Puffball)

INEDIBLE

HABITAT Autumn. In coniferous and hardwood forests, particularly oak. On the ground.

GENERAL APPEARANCE At first it resembles a small tulip bulb or onion. It is enveloped by a thick, yellowish or smoky covering. The upper part of this covering splits radially into a star pattern forming from six to nine triangular lobes that are more or less regular in shape. These lobes may open like the petals of a daisy and they may then close back again on the central onion-shaped mass of the fungus. When the weather is damp these lobes open into a star shape and curl back toward the ground. With their points resting on the ground they may even raise the central portion of the fungus off the ground. When the weather turns dry again, the lobes curl back again and curl over the central portion of the fungus once again. These lobes are thick. The surface facing the central portion of the fungus is pale brown and fleshy; the surface facing outward is smooth and whitish. The central portion of the fungus is enveloped by a second covering that is thin, membranous, smoky white, and fragile. It is surmounted by a small conical umbo. When the fungus is mature this umbo splits in the form of a crater mouth with a dentellate, fringed, and floccose margin. The inner substance, pulverulent by now and tobacco brown in color, begins to come out this aperture.

MISTAKEN For **Geastrum rufescens**, likewise inedible, which can be distinguished by its lobes. These lobes are reddish at first, turning reddish brown. The lobes crack and split transversely as well as the fungus matures.

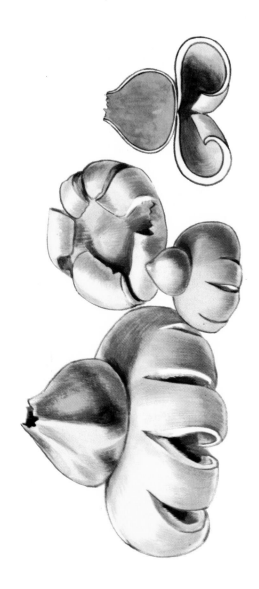

Geastrum fimbriatum (Fringed Geaster)

INEDIBLE Harmless in small quantities; poisonous in larger quantities. It is not likely that anyone could eat large quantities of this fungus.

HABITAT Summer and autumn. In woodlands and clearings. On sandy, dry, and sterile ground. On old stumps, between the roots of old stumps, or on the ground nearby. Occasionally one may find **Boletus parasiticus** 131 growing parasitically on this fungus. This Bolete is also inedible.

GENERAL APPEARANCE It resembles a small compressed sphere or a compressed egg, lying on the ground. It is usually no larger than a nut, but may be as large as a small tangerine. From 1 to 5 inches in diameter.

OUTER COVERING Yellowish, ochre, hazel, or reddish in color, later turning brownish ochre. Elastic at first, turning leathery and rugose, entirely covered with coarse flattened warts darker in color than the rest of the covering. When cut, these warts show up pink or pale reddish inside. From 3/4 to 1 1/2 inches in thickness. When the fungus is mature, this covering cracks irregularly on top. The inner substance, which has turned into olive gray or greenish spores by this time, gradually begins to emerge from this opening.

STALK This fungus does not have a genuine stalk. It rests directly on the ground and has a small bunch of rootlike filaments growing into the ground.

FLESH The inner substance is firm and white, turning pink and finally blackish indigo with some whitish veining. Then the flesh becomes pulverulent and clotted and olive gray in color. Then it gradually issues from the opening at the top, of the outer covering. It has a strong and disgusting odor.

MISTAKEN For the equally inedible **Scleroderma verrucosum**, which does not rest directly on the ground but is supported by a distinct stalk that is squat and thick, grooved and covered with branching ribs that make it resemble a tiny oak trunk. Furthermore **verrucosum** has, instead of large warts, very fine, granulose, and close warts on the outer covering. **Scleroderma aurantium** may also be mistaken for various puffballs which are white inside when young and later turn olive brown, but which never turn black indigo.

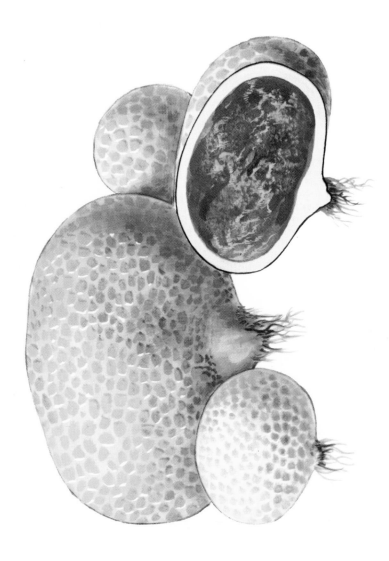

Scleroderma aurantium (Common Scleroderma)

169 GYROCEPHALUS RUFUS PHLOGIOTUS HELVELLOIDES

GOOD   As long as the fungus is immature, it can even be eaten raw in salad. When it is very mature, it is tough and indigestible and must be cooked for a long time, though it is still inferior.

HABITAT   From spring until the beginning of winter, but chiefly in summer and autumn. In mountains. In woods, especially fir. In damp sheltered places, in the grass or on mossy ground, and on decaying plant detritus. Usually in large clusters and frequently in groups of clusters.

CAP   It resembles a standing dog ear or a spatula or a funnel open on one side. From 1-4³⁄₄ inches in height; from 1-4³⁄₄ inches in width. It is thin, gelatinous, elastic, and translucid. The inner surface is smooth; the outer surface is rugose and almost grooved by thin flat veining. Both surfaces are orange pink or flesh pink in color.

STALK   Often there is no real stalk at all but a simple rootlet attaching the body of the fungus to the earth, cylindrical and somewhat paler in color than the cap.

FLESH   Thin, gelatinous, translucid, elastic, and quite tough. Paler than the color of the outer walls. Faint odor and mild taste.

Gyrocephalus rufus (Apricot Jelly Mushroom)
Phlogiotus helvelloides

(Morel; Sponge Mushroom)

EXCELLENT Discard mature specimens with withered caps and yellowish stalks, even those that are only partially withered or altered. These specimens may cause serious disturbances. Clean off the sand and young snails. The fungi must be carefully cooked. One should eat small quantities, for excessive consumption might be dangerous. This fungus may also be dried.

HABITAT Spring, especially if the weather is warm and dry; rarely in autumn. In mountainous regions and in the plains. In hardwood forests, especially elm and ash. At the edge of clearings, in shady and cool pasturelands; on the edge of fields; and even in vineyards. Pratically on sandy ground. Solitary or gregarious. When gregarious it may grow in rows or rings.

CAP Globose and resembling an enormous strawberry. From 1 1/2-2 1/4 inches in diameter. Completely covered with pits resembling the inner surface of a beehive. The pits may be angular or polygonal or rounded, and they are arranged in no particular order. They are framed by irregularly arranged ribbing elements. The pits themselves are usually ochre in color, while the ribbing is usually yellowish. Hence the over-all color is pale ochre. It may also be reddish or olive in color. The inside of the cap is hollow and empty. The inner wall of the cap is off-white and covered with furfuraceous flocculi.

STALK Cylindrical and much larger at the base; somewhat choked under the cap. From 1 1/2-3 inches in height; from 3/4-1 1/2 in diameter. Rugose and wrinkly. Longitudinally grooved. Just beneath the cap, the stem is covered with furfuraceous flocculi. Whitish, turning ochraceous. Fragile. Hollow and empty.
FLESH Fragile. It has the appearance and consistency of wax. White. The odor is slight, and the taste is pleasant.

MISTAKEN HARMLESSLY For other **Morchellae**, which are also excellent.

Morchella esculanta (Morel)

EXCELLENT   Discard mature specimens with withered caps and yellowish stalks, even if they are only slightly altered. They may cause serious disturbance. They should be cleaned to remove dirt and small snails. They should be well cooked. One should eat only moderate quantities. Excessive consumption might be dangerous. This fungus may also be dried.

HABITAT   Spring. In mountainous regions and in the plains. In fir woods; on the edge of elm and ash woods; in orchards, especially apple; on ground in which bones have been buried; and even on playing fields. Gregarious, in large groups.

CAP   Ovoid at first, then becoming somewhat oblong. From 1-3½ inches in height; from 3/4-2 inches in diameter. The cap is closely and irregularly pitted, and the pitting becomes deeper as the fungus matures. These pits are divided by ribbing that descends from the top of the cap to the margin, though not all of the ribbings reach the margin. These ribbings become more prominent as the fungus matures. The general appearance of the cap suggests a sponge. The general color of the ribbing and the pits is blackish gray, becoming lighter and finally ochraceous, sometimes copper ochre in color. Inside the cap is hollow and empty; the walls of this cavity are pale ashy in color.

STALK   Cylindrical and very irregular in shape. From 3/4-2½ inches in height; from 1/2-1½ inches in diameter. It is often disjointed. The base is swollen. There are deep longitudinal grooves that are deepest toward the base. Whitish and covered with furfuraceous matter; then glabrous; ochraceous or light copper-ochre in color. The stalk is hollow and empty; and the walls of the stalk cavity are whitish and floccose.

FLESH   It has the appearance and consistency of wax. It is somewhat paler in color than the outer surface of the stalk. The odor is pleasant but faint. The taste is mild and pleasant.

N. B.   The characteristics that distinguish **Morchella vulgaris** from **Morchella deliciosa** 172 are accidental and not specific. Hence they should not be considered two different species.

Excellent

Morchella vulgaris (Morel)

EXCELLENT Discard mature specimens with withered caps and yellowish stalks, even if they are only slightly altered. They may cause serious disturbance. They should be cleaned to remove dirt and small snails. They should be well cooked. One should eat only moderate quantities. Excessive consumption might be dangerous. This fungus may also be dried.

HABITAT Spring. In mountainous regions. In coniferous woods, especially fir. In grassy clearing, in pastures, and on the edge of clearings. Gregarious, in large groups.

CAP Oval or oval-conical, sometimes with a cuspidate top. From 1½-3 inches in height; from 1-2 inches in diameter. Ribbing runs down from the cusp and joined by transverse ribbings, short and less numerous. They form pits that are generally oblong or rectangular, small and close. As the fungus matures, the ribbing blackens. The over-all color of the cap is smoky yellow, turning smoky hazel-gray, then olive brown, and finally blackish brown. The interior of the cap is hollow and empty; the walls of the cap cavity are whitish and flocculose. There is a definite groove, almost a step, between the cap and the stalk.

STALK Cylindrical with a bulbous base and marked by clear grooves. From 1-2 inches in height; from 1/4-1¼ inches in diameter. White and covered with fine scales or furfuraceous matter; later becoming glabrous and yellowish. Hollow and empty; the walls of the stalk cavity are very flocculose.

FLESH It has the appearance and consistency of wax. Hence it is fragile. The flesh of the cap is white with pink tinges; that of the stalk is white. The odor is mild, and the taste is pleasant.

MISTAKEN HARMLESSLY For other **Morchellae**, all excellent.

N. B. The characteristics that distinguish **Morchella deliciosa** from **Morchella vulgaris** 171 are accidental and not specific. Hence they should not be considered two different species.

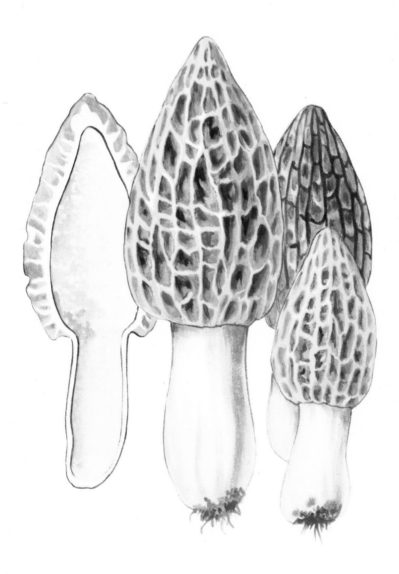

Morchella deliciosa (Morel)

EXCELLENT Discard mature specimens with withered caps and yellowish stalks, even if they are only slightly altered. They may cause serious disturbance. They should be cleaned to remove dirt and small snails. They should be well cooked. One should eat only moderate quantities. Excessive consumption might be dangerous. This fungus may also be dried.

HABITAT Spring. Although it grows in the plains, it is more common in mountainous regions. In woods, especially coniferous. Gregarious, it may grow in large groups.

CAP Conical with a pointed apex. From 1-2 1/2 inches in height; from 3/4-1 1/2 inches in diameter. Pitted all over. The pits are irregular in form, some are angular and some are rounded; the color is olive chestnut. These pits are framed by longitudinal ribbing coming down from the apex to the margin of the cap; this ribbing is olive black. Transverse ribbing branches out from the vertical ribbing. There is further, less pronounced ribbing that enters the pits without joining other transverse ribbing. The cap altogether resembles a conical sponge. The over-all color is brownish or olive. The cap is hollow and empty; the inner walls are whitish and covered with a very thin layer of flocculose or furfuraceous matter. There is a clearly defined groove or step between the cap and the stalk.

STALK Cylindrical. From 3/4-1 1/2 inches in height; from 3/4-1 1/4 inches in diameter. Robust. It sometimes tapers toward the base, but on occasion it broadens at the base. There are more or less pronounced longitudinal grooves. Whitish or pale copper in color. Velvety or furfuraceous or slightly scaly. The stalk is hollow and empty. The inner walls are covered with flocculi or furfuraceous matter.

FLESH It has the appearance and consistency of wax. The flesh of the cap is white at first but turns darker. That of the stalk is always off-white in color. The odor is mild and the taste is pleasant.

MISTAKEN HARMLESSLY For other **Morchellae**, equally excellent.

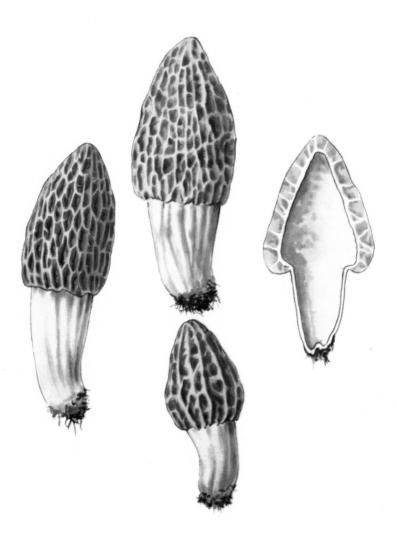

Morchella conica (Morel)

174 MITROPHORA HYBRIDA
MORCHELLA SEMILIBRA

(Half-free Morel)

GOOD   Discard mature specimens with withered caps and yellowish stems, even if they are only slightly altered. They may cause serious disturbance. They should be cleaned inside and out to remove dirt and small snails. They should be well cooked.

HABITAT   In the months of May and June. In woodlands, especially near poplars. Along footpaths, watercourses, and in the grass. Often in large groups.

CAP   Conical with a pointed apex. From 1-2½ inches in height; from 3/4-1½ inches in diameter. The cap is covered with oblong or rectangular pitting. The pittings that descends from the apex of the cap to the margin in fairly regular pattern. There are transverse ribbings, but these are less pronounced. The pits are grayish brown, yellowish brown, or olive brown inside; the ribbing is almost black. The over-all color is grayish brown, reddish brown, or olive brown. The cap margin is not attached to the stalk, but it descends roof-gutter-fashion around it. The cap is hollow and empty, and the walls of this cavity are pale ashy and flocculose.

STALK   Cylindrical. From 1-2½ inches in height; from 1/3-3/4 inches in diameter. Quite swollen at the base. Very rugose, especially just under the cap. Whitish and covered with furfuraceous matter or delicate scales. It turns faded yellow and is longitudinally wrinkled. Hollow and empty. The walls of the stalk cavity are off-white, ashy, or yellowish in color; covered with furfuraceous matter or small scales.

FLESH   Soft, watery, and fragile. The odor is faint and the taste is mild.

MISTAKEN HARMLESLY   For the variety **rimosipes**, a good fungus with a cap that is relatively smaller than that of **hybrida** and a stalk that may be 6-8 inches tall.

Mitrophora hybrida (Half-free Morel)
Morchella semilibra

DEADLY When raw. It is just as poisonous, even deadly, when cooked if eaten at two meals taken close together.

GOOD And harmless if eaten cooked at a single meal and not consumed in large quantity. It can be dried. Drying removes its poisonous qualities at least as much as cooking. If one does not want to consume this fungus dried but fresh, one should proceed in the following manner. It should be boiled in water for a few minutes, well drained, and then cooked carefully with appropriate seasoning. It should not be eaten in large quantity. One should not eat it a second time until at least three or four days have passed since it was eaten a first time. There is no need to boil the mushroom before preparing it if it has been dried. But these dried mushrooms should not be mature specimens and they should have dried out spontaneously on the ground. They must be young specimens, picked when young, and set to dry only if they are perfectly sound specimens.

N. B. If one has never eaten **Gyromitra** before, one should eat only a small amount the first time as a test. Only later, when several days have passed and when one is certain that he is not especially susceptible to the substances contained in this fungus, should one eat larger quantities.

HABITAT From March till May; rarely in the autumn. In coniferous woods. In cool, damp, and sandy places. At the base of old stumps, and also in fields and along the edge of roads. Gregarious, sometimes in large groups.

CAP Irregular in form; usually divided into three or four lobes; grooved by ribbed convolutions that make it resemble a knotty brain. From 1-3 inches in height; from 1-3 inches in diameter. It is brownish yellow, turning chestnut or reddish brown. It is hollow and whitish inside.

STALK Irregular. From 1-3 inches in height. Tuberose and gibbose. Sometimes it narrows toward the top. Usually compressed. Grooved by wrinkles, particularly at the base. Off-white, turning pink. Covered with furfuraceous matter or covered with fine down. Full at first, then hollow.

FLESH Fragile. It has the appearance and the consistency of wax. Whitish, turning pink. The odor is mild, and the taste is faint.

Good with great caution

Gyromitra esculenta (Brain Mushroom)

GOOD As long as it is gathered when young and then perfectly cooked. When it is somewhat matured it is leathery and indigestible.

HABITAT From August until November. In coniferous and hardwood forests. In damp sheltered places. In grassy clearings, along pits and footpaths. Solitary or gregarious.

CAP Thin. It has the form of a tricorn hat, a bishop's miter, a turban, or a rag tossed on the top of a small pole. From 3/4-1 1/2 inches in height; from 1-2 inches in width. At first the margin adheres to the stalk; then it becomes detached and curls up in unpredictable forms. The upper surface is glabrous, very rugose, and irregular; off-white in color or pale. The lower surface is covered with furfuraceous matter and is hazel in color.

STALK Cylindrical and very irregular. Sometimes it is swelling at the base. It is covered with longitudinal grooves and prominent ridges or veins that occasionally join in net patterns. From 1-2 3/4 inches in height; from 1/2-1 1/4 inches in diameter. White, turning yellowish. Hollow. The stalk walls are thin.

FLESH Thin, firm, tough, and white. The odor is pleasant, and the taste is mild.

N. B. There are various other species of fungi of the genus **Helvellae**; they are less frequent, smaller, and edible. Among these are the **Helvella elastica**, with a slender and hollow stalk, a yellowish upper surface to the cap and a whitish lower surface, and the **Helvella monachella**, which has a slender and hollow stem, a blackish violet upper surface to the cap and a whitish lower surface.

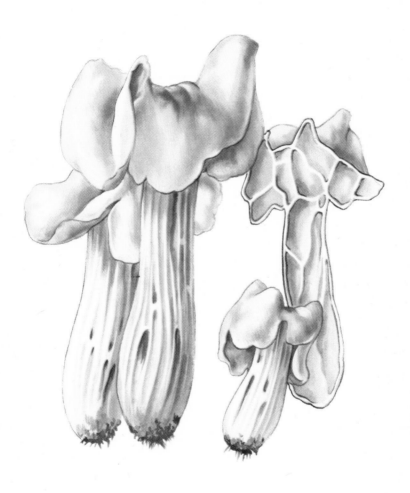

Helvella crispa (Common Helvella)

(Elfin Saddle)

EDIBLE   But rather hard.

HABITAT   Summer and autumn. In woodlands and damp places. Along footpaths. On the ground near rotting trunks. On grassy or mossy ground. Usually in groups, but occasionally solitary.

CAP   It has the form of a tricorn hat, a bishop's miter, a turban, or a rag tossed on the top of a small pole. From 3/4-1½ inches in height; from 3/4-1½ inches in width. The margin is bizarrely lobed, cuspidate, wrinkled, and twisted. The upper surface is rough and smoky-ashy or blackish in color. The lower surface is smooth and ashy in color.

STALK   Cylindrical and irregular. From 3/4-1½ inches in height; from 1/3-3/4 inches in diameter. It is covered with longitudinal grooves and prominent ridges or veins that occasionally join in net patterns. Thus it resembles an old oak trunk in miniature. It is ashy in color but lighter toward the base. At first it is full of a cottony substance; later it is hollow. The stalk walls are thin.

FLESH   Thin, tough, white or tending to ashy gray. It is almost odorless and tasteless.

N. B.   There are various other less frequent species of fungi of the genus **Helvellae**; they are generally smaller and are edible. Among these are the **Helvella elastica**, with a slender and hollow stalk, a yellowish upper surface to the cap and a whitish lower surface; and the **Helvella monachella**, which has a slender and hollow stalk, a blackish violet upper surface to the cap and a whitish lower surface.

Edible

Helvella lacunosa (Elfin Saddle)

178 HELVELLA INFULA
GYROMITRA INFULA

(Hooded Helvella)

EDIBLE WITH CAUTION   Since this fungus may cause some disturbances, albeit not alarming, in some people. Anyone eating this fungus for the first time should take only small quantities.

HABITAT   Autumn, and sometimes in spring. In coniferous and hradwood forests, especially beech. In damp places. On the ground near decaying stumps and decaying plant detritus.

CAP   Thin. From 2-4 inches. It has curled and shriveled lobes, some standing erect like horns and others falling over the stalk. The upper surface is covered with furfuraceous matter and is whitish in color.

STALK   Cylindrical or in the form of an inverted cone. It is covered with longitudinal grooves and irregular ridges. Whitish or pale in color and covered with whitish down. At first it is full of a cottony substance; then it is hollow and subdivided into various cavities. When it is hollow it is often also compressed.

FLESH   It has the appearance and cosistency of wax. Fragile. The odor and taste are pleasant.

N. B.   There are various other, less frequent species of fungi of the genus **Helvella**; they are generally smaller and are edible. Among these are the **Helvella elastica**, with a slender and hollow stalk, a yellowish upper surface to the cap and a whitish lower surface; and the **Helvella monachella**, which has a slender and hollow stalk, a blackish violet upper surface to the cap and a whitish lower surface.

Helvella (Gyromitra) infula (Hooded Helvella)

PEZIZA ACETABULUM
PAXINA ACETABULUM   (Reticulated Peziza)

INEDIBLE   Raw, because it causes disturbances.

EDIBLE   Only when it has been well cooked.

HABITAT   Spring. In woods, especially oak. Along footpaths. In fertilized places. Gregarious, often in large groups.

GENERAL APPEARANCE   It is more or less regularly cup shaped. It is supported by a stalk that is clearly distict from the cap. The cap may achieve a diameter of from 1-2¾ inches. The margin is undulate and lobed, usually at least in part, and curves up toward the inside of the cap. The inner surface is brown or olive brown, darkening toward the center. The outer surface is grayish at first, turning brown but usually lighter than the inner surface. It is covered with furfuraceous matter.

STALK   It resembles an old oak trunk in miniature: squat, thick, longitudinally grooved and ridged. The ridging even envelops part of the cap. It is faded gray in color. The stalk is hollow and subdivided into many vertical cavities.

FLESH   Thin and whitish. Indefinable odor. Mild taste.

MISTAKEN HARMLESSLY   For the edible **Peziza (Disciotis) venosa** 180, which does not have a genuine stalk supporting the cap and has noticeable veining inside the cap.

Edible with caution

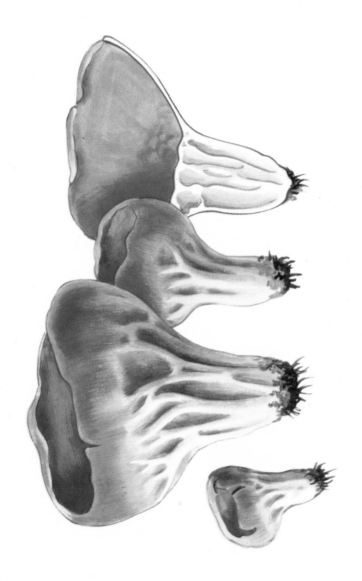

Peziza (Paxina) acetabulum (Reticulated Peziza)

180 PEZIZA VENOSA
DISCIOTIS VENOSA

INEDIBLE   When raw it causes disturbances.

GOOD   Only when well cooked.

HABITAT   Spring. In woodlands. On the edge of woods. Along footpaths. Gregarious, sometimes in very large groups.

GENERAL APPEARANCE   It has the form of a more or less regular cup. The largest diameter is from 1-6 inches. The margin is often undulate and lobed; usually at least part of the margin is turned toward the inside of the cup. The inner surface darkens in color from pale brown until it is chestnut, blackish brown or blackish olive. From the center of the cup emanate large veins that extend toward but do not reach the margin. The outer surface is whitish at first, turning browner but usually lighter than the inner surface.

STALK   It does not have a genuine stalk supporting the cup. There is a small rootlet that grows into the ground; it is whitish in color and is marked by large rounded ridges that ascend toward the cup.

FLESH   Thin and whitish. The odor is similar to that of lye or some soaps. The taste is mild.

MISTAKEN HARMLESSLY   For the edible **Peziza (Paxina) acetabulum** 179, which has a genuine stalk and does not have noticeable veining inside the cup.

Good with caution

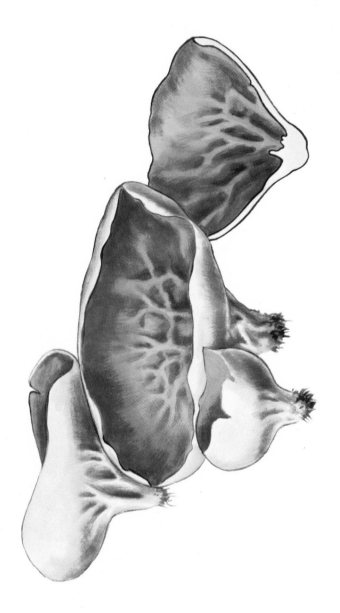

Peziza (Disciotis) venosa (Veined Peziza)

PEZIZA AURANTIA   (Orange Fairy-cup; Orange-peel Peziza)
         ALEURIA AURANTIA

GOOD   Even raw in salad.

HABITAT   Autumn. In sparse woods and along shady roads. On clayish and sandy ground. In the grass. Gregarious.

GENERAL APPEARANCE   This fungus first appears in the form of a small, hollow, pinkish white sphere with delicate furfuraceous matter on the surface. Then it opens and becomes bowl shaped. The inner surface is a bright orange-red color, and the outer surface is whitish pink and phosphorescent. Then it expands farther and takes on the appearance of an oyster shell or auricle; it may take on unexpected forms as well. The margin is undulate and lobed. The greatest dimension when the fungus is fully mature is between 1-4 inches. It has no stalk and rests directly on the ground. It has thin walls a few millimeters thick. They are fragile, fleshy, and the color of the flesh is reddish. The odor is pleasant and the taste is mild.

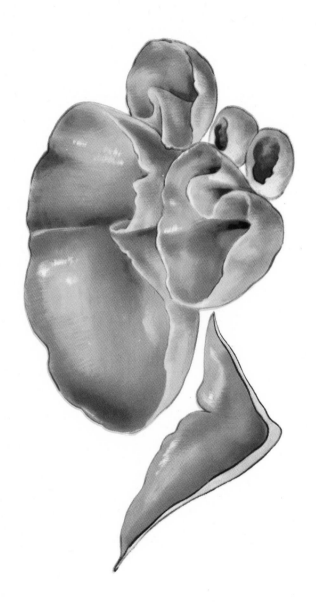

Good

Peziza (Aleuria) aurantia (Orange Fairy-cup)

182 PEZIZA ONOTICA
OTIDEA ONOTICA

(Orange-ear Peziza)

EDIBLE

HABITAT Summer and autumn. In woods, especially oak and beech. On sandy ground. Clusters and groups of clusters.

GENERAL APPEARANCE It resembles a donkey ear or a rabbit ear, narrowing toward the base. The base is short, covered with down, and grows into the earth. It may be as much as 4 inches tall and 2 ¼ inches wide. The margin is undulate and sometimes lobed. The outer surface is glabrous and yellow. The inner surface is light orange-yellow or ochre yellow with pink tinges.

FLESH Thin. Waxy. Yellow. The odor is faint and the taste is mild.

MISTAKEN HARMLESSLY For the equally edible species **leporina**, which has one side taller than the other and grows less vertically than **Peziza** (**Otidea**) **onotica**.

Peziza (Otidea) onotica (Orange-ear Peziza)

183 PEZIZA EXIMIA
SARCOSPHAERA EXEMIA

POISONOUS   When raw or improperly cooked or even slightly spoiled.

EDIBLE   As long as the fungus is perfectly sound and perfectly cooked.

HABITAT   In plains, from spring till the beginning of summer, most commonly under pines, on limey-sandy soil. It grows in mountainous regions, in the summertime, usually under firs on limey-sandy soil.

GENERAL APPEARANCE   First it appears in the form of a spherical or egg-shaped ball almost buried in the earth; it is empty and closed. Then this ball bursts, beginning at the top, and splits into several triangular or oval lobes that often come to a point and are sometimes jagged along the margin. Gradually these lobes open up and become larger. The fungus then is almost totally outside the ground and may have a diameter of from 1½-5 or even 7 inches. The inner surface is lilac white at first, then turning ever darker purple in color as the fungus matures. The outer surface is yellowish white; glabrous or delicately velvety.

STALK   It does not have a genuine stalk. The base on the ground is yellowish; from it extends a rootlike appendage.

FLESH   Thin, fragile, and violet white. The odor is faint and the taste is mild.

Peziza (Sarcosphaera) eximia

EDIBLE But inferior.

HABITAT From late summer until late autumn. In mountainous regions. In coniferous woods, especially fir and pine. On needles fallen from conifers and among moss. Gregarious, in groups or long rows.

GENERAL APPEARANCE It may resemble a whitish or yellowish cigarette butt topped by a yellow wig, half moon or horseshoe-shaped magnet. It may also resemble a coarse yellow spatula with a short whitish or yellowish handle.

CAP Ovoid like a horseshoe. The largest diameter is from 1/2-1 1/4 inches. It is set athwart the stem. Smooth. It is often divided into 2 or 3 lobes. Yellow.

STALK Clearly distinct from the cap. Cylindrical. It may be quite irregular in form. Usually short and squat. From 1/2-2 inches in height. Whitish or yellowish.

FLESH That of the cap is yellow; that of the stalk is whitish or yellowish. There is no particular odor, and the taste is not very pleasant.

Spathularia flavida (Yellow Spathularia)

EXCELLENT This most exquisite of all the truffles has not been found in the United States.

HABITAT Summer, autumn, and winter. In northern and central Italy and in some areas of France. In oak, poplar, willow, and linden forests. On limey ground. Buried in the ground at various depths at the foot of various trees. Solitary or gregarious. Truffles are found by scenting dogs or pigs especially trained for truffle hunting.

GENERAL APPEARANCE It usually resembles a potato and may be gibbose, tuberous, sometimes with depressed lobes radiating from the center. The cuticle that covers the tuber is thin and can only be removed by peeling as if it were a potato. It is ochre or brownish ochre in color. Smooth or covered with minute papillae that are slightly darker in color.

FLESH Compact and soapy in consistency. The flesh of the young fungus is white; then it turns silvery pink and finally a slightly smoky violet gray. It often has patches of slightly darker color. It is grooved with whitish veining of varying size. Usually the veining is filiform and its meanders creat a bizarre and close net pattern. The odor is strong, pungent, and garlic-like or similar to that of Gorgonzola cheese. The taste is pleasant. In only a few weeks the flesh becomes tender, then flaccid, and finally decomposes.

N. B. There are many other species of fungus that grow underground. Some are poisonous but not deadly poisonous. They may cause stomachache, nausea, vomiting, diarrhea - varying in intensity.

Tuber magnatum (Piedmont's Truffle)

EXCELLENT This truffle has not been found in the United States.

HABITAT Summer, autumn, and winter. In regions where grapevines can grow. In sparse woods or oak, chestnut, poplar, beech, hazelnut and other hardwood trees. On limey ground. Under the ground at the foot of trees at various depths. Truffles are found by scenting dogs or pigs especially trained for truffle hunting.

GENERAL APPEARANCE At first sight it resembles a block of coke coal, globular or oval, often irregular with tuberous lumps and lobes. From 1-6 inches in diameter. The cuticle is very thin and can be peeled as one would a potato. It is brownish black; when struck it turns rust colored. It is completely covered with polygonal warts, about 1-2 inches across, equal in size and usually with a depressed apex. The warts are black with greenish brown spots or lines; slightly crumbly.

FLESH White first, but soon turning grayish, then violaceous gray, then brown gray, and finally, when the fungus is fully mature, brownish black. It is grooved with veins that are white at first but turn reddish. Filiform and clearly defined, the veins form a tight network. The odor is strong, pungent, and characteristic. The taste is slightly bitterish but pleasant.

MISTAKEN HARMLESSLY For the **Tuber aestivum**, which is also excellent, but that truffle has much lighter flesh when mature than the **Tuber melanosporum** does.

N. B. There are many other species of fungus that frow underground. Some are poisonous but not deadly poisonous. The may cause stomach ache, nausea, vomiting, diarrhea, varying in intensity.

Tuber melanosporum (Winter Truffle)

INDEX

(Reference numbers in italics refer to pages in the introductory sections; all others refer to the numbers assigned in the catalogue portion of the book.)

437

36252